Beatles Hits *arranged for* ukulele

Wise Publications
part of The Music Sales Group
London/New York/Paris/Sydney/Copenhagen/Berlin/Madrid/Tokyo

Published by:
Wise Publications,
14-15 Berners Street, London W1T 3LJ, UK.

Exclusive Distributors:
Music Sales Limited,
Distribution Centre, Newmarket Road, Bury St Edmunds,
Suffolk IP33 3YB, UK.
Music Sales Pty Limited,
20 Resolution Drive, Caringbah, NSW 2229, Australia.

Order No. NO91223
ISBN 978-1-84772-663-6

Edited by David Harrison.
Music engraved by Paul Ewers Music Design.
Cover designed by Fresh Lemon.
Photographs courtesy of Matthew Ward.

Printed in the EU.

Your Guarantee of Quality
As publishers, we strive to produce every book to the highest
commercial standards.

The music has been freshly engraved and the book has been carefully designed
to minimise awkward page turns and to make playing from it a real pleasure.

Particular care has been given to specifying acid-free, neutral-sized
paper made from pulps which have not been elemental chlorine bleached.

This pulp is from farmed sustainable forests and was produced with
special regard for the environment.

Throughout, the printing and binding have been planned to ensure
a sturdy, attractive publication which should give years of enjoyment.

If your copy fails to meet our high standards, please inform us
and we will gladly replace it.

www.musicsales.com

across the universe

Words & Music by John Lennon & Paul McCartney

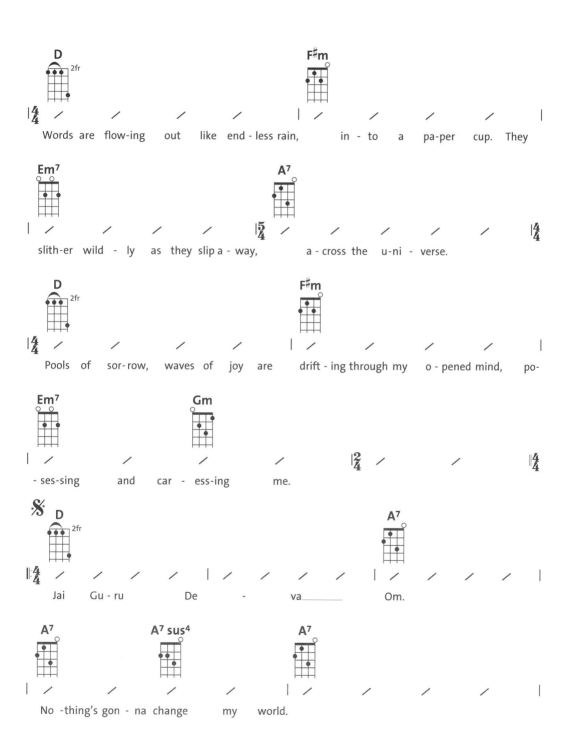

Words are flow-ing out like end-less rain, in-to a pa-per cup. They slith-er wild-ly as they slip a-way, a-cross the u-ni-verse.

Pools of sor-row, waves of joy are drift-ing through my o-pened mind, po- ses-sing and car-ess-ing me.

Jai Gu-ru De - va____ Om.

No-thing's gon-na change my world.

G | D

Noth - ing's gon - na change my world.

A7 | A7 sus4 | A7

Noth - ing's gon - na change my world.

G | D

To Coda ⊕

No - thing's gon - na change my world.

1.

F♯m

I-mag - es_ of bro-ken light, which dance be-fore me like a mil - lion eyes,

Em7 | A7

___ they call me on and on_ a - cross___ the u-ni - verse.

D | F♯m

Thoughts me-an - der like a rest - less wind in - side a let-ter box, they

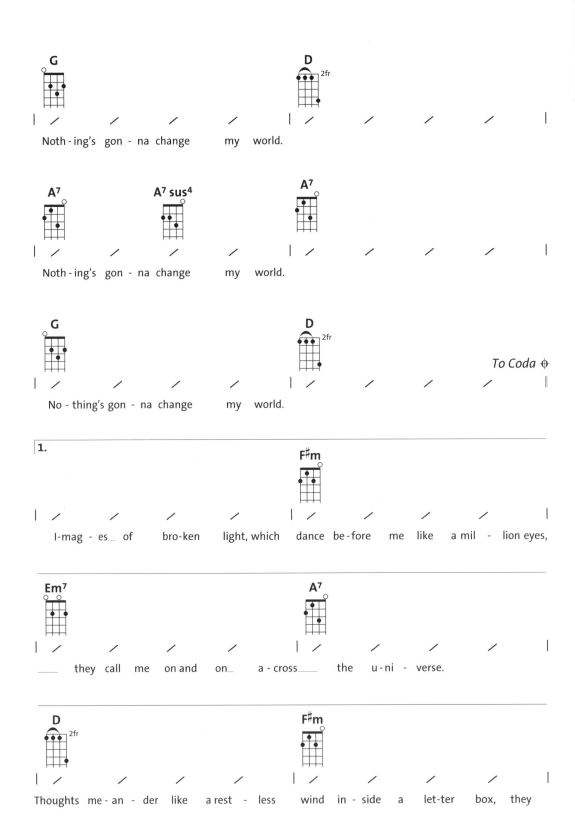

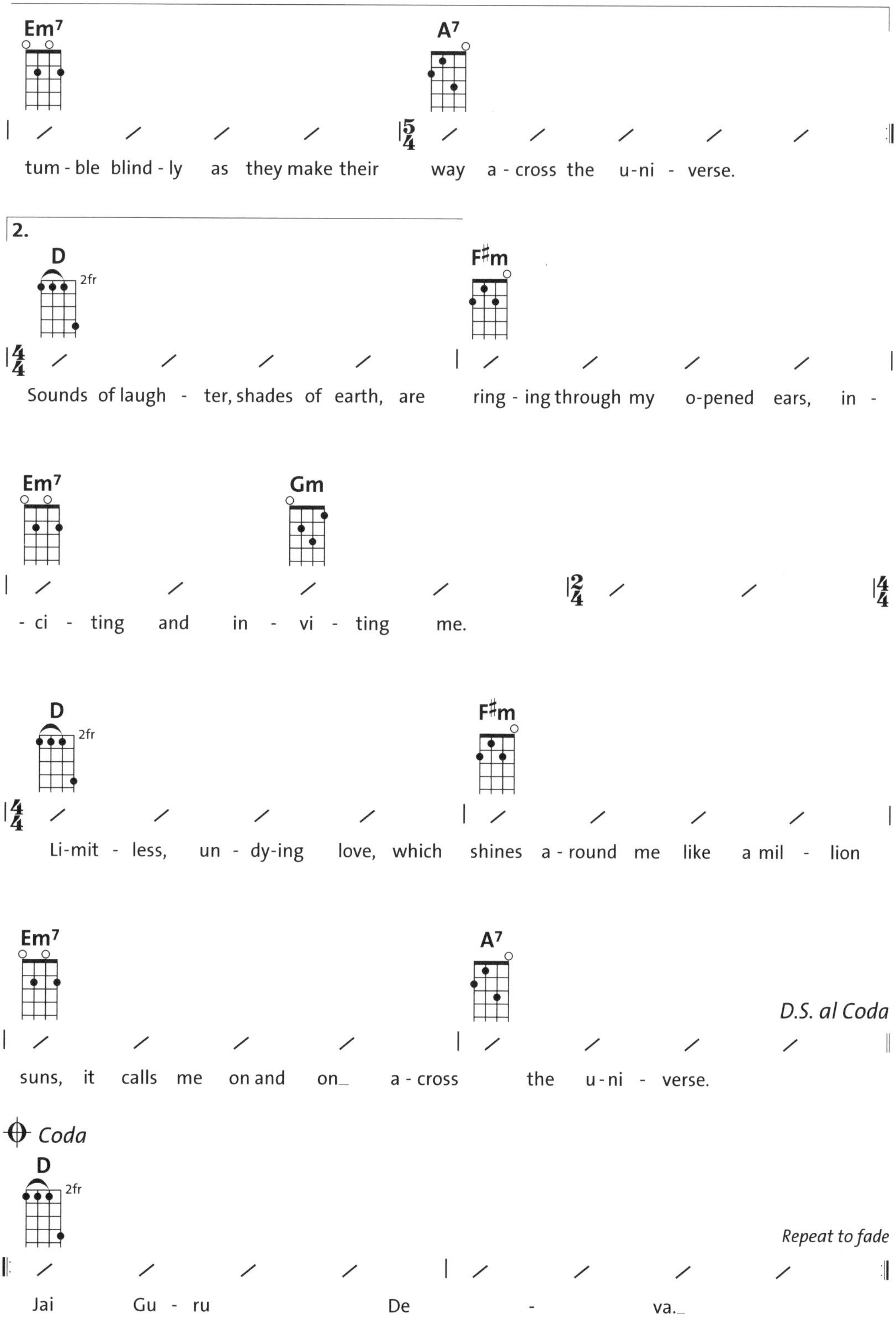
Em7
A7
tum - ble blind - ly as they make their way a - cross the u - ni - verse.
2.
D
2fr
F♯m
Sounds of laugh - ter, shades of earth, are ring - ing through my o-pened ears, in -
Em7
Gm
- ci - ting and in - vi - ting me.
D
2fr
F♯m
Li-mit - less, un - dy-ing love, which shines a - round me like a mil - lion
Em7
A7
D.S. al Coda
suns, it calls me on and on_ a - cross the u - ni - verse.
Coda
D
2fr
Repeat to fade
Jai Gu - ru De - va._

all my loving

Words & Music by John Lennon & Paul McCartney

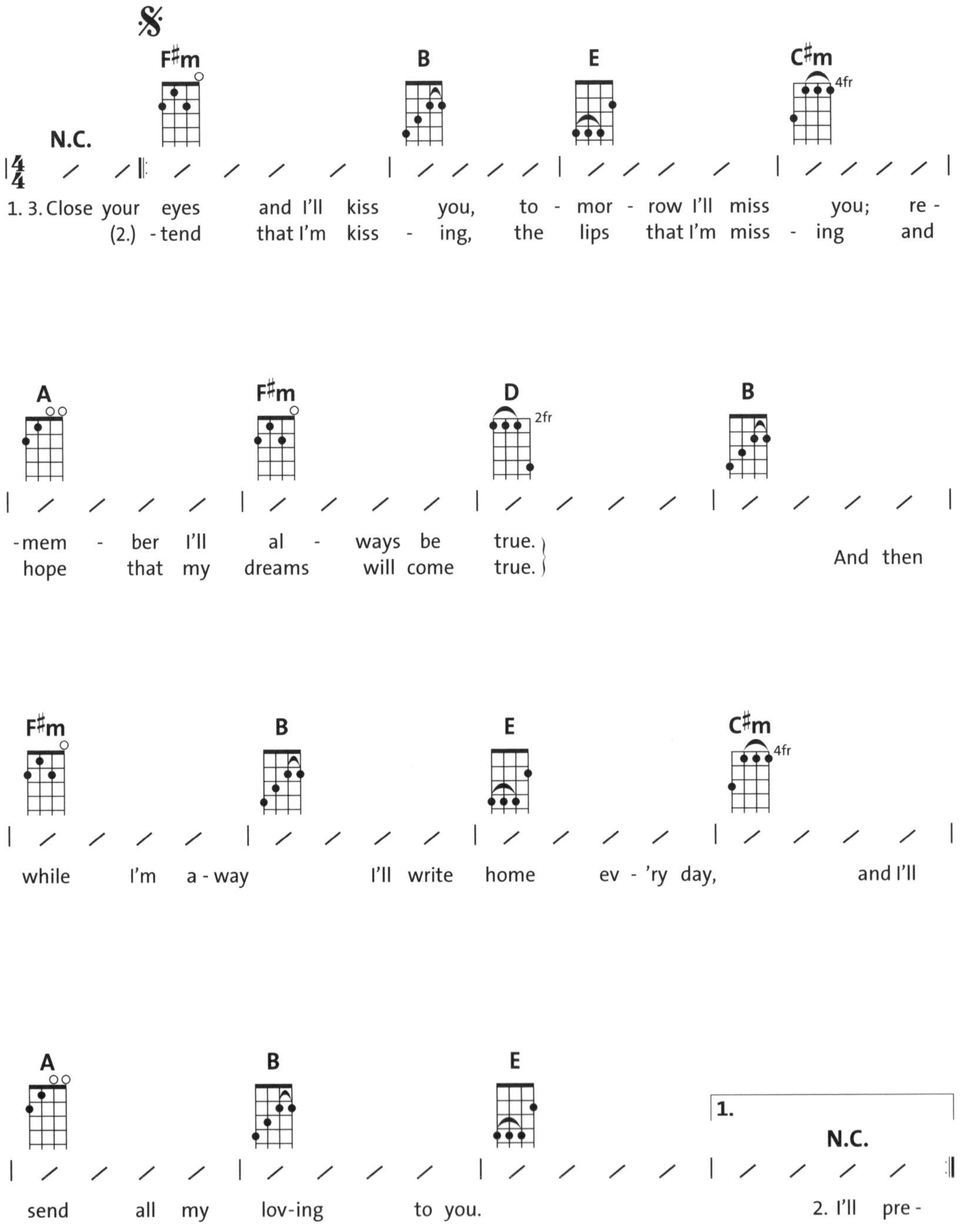

N.C.
F♯m
B
E
C♯m
4fr
1. 3. Close your eyes and I'll kiss you, to - mor - row I'll miss you; re -
(2.) - tend that I'm kiss - ing, the lips that I'm miss - ing and
A
F♯m
D
2fr
B
- mem - ber I'll al - ways be true.
hope that my dreams will come true.
And then
F♯m
B
E
C♯m
4fr
while I'm a - way I'll write home ev - 'ry day, and I'll
A
B
E
1.
N.C.
send all my lov-ing to you.
2. I'll pre -

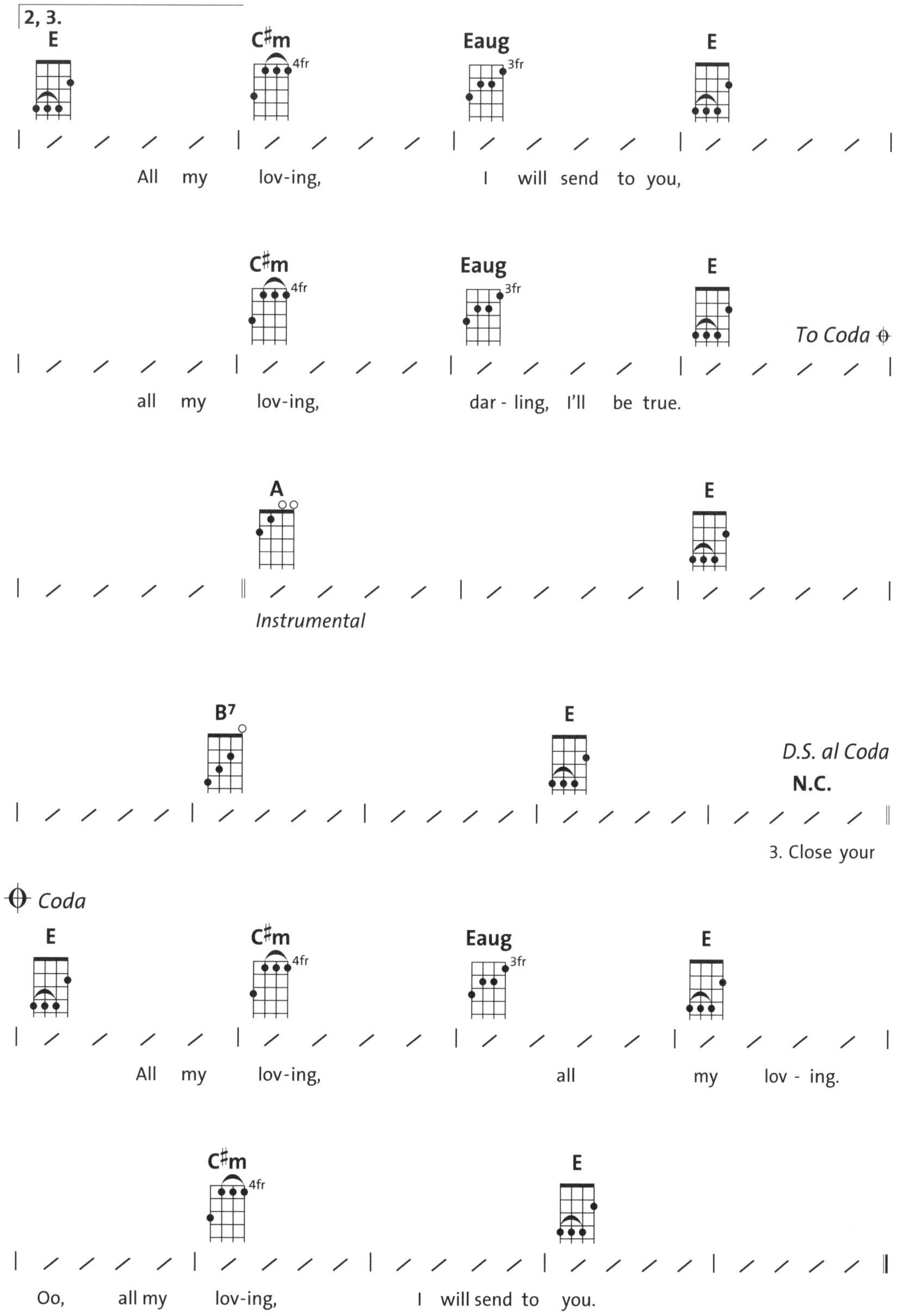

All my lov-ing, I will send to you,

all my lov-ing, dar - ling, I'll be true.

To Coda ⊕

Instrumental

D.S. al Coda

N.C.

3. Close your

⊕ *Coda*

All my lov-ing, all my lov - ing.

Oo, all my lov-ing, I will send to you.

eleanor rigby

Words & Music by John Lennon & Paul McCartney

C | **Em**

4/4 Ah, look at all the lone - ly peo - ple.

𝄋

Em | **Em7**

1. E - lea - nor Rig - by, picks up the rice in the church
2. Fa - ther Mc Ken - zie, writ - ing the words of a ser -
3. E - lea - or Rig - by, died in the church and was bu -

Em6 | **C** | **Em**

where a wed - ding has been, lives in a dream.
\- mon that no one will hear, no one comes near.
\- ried a - long with her name, no - bo - dy came.

Em7

Waits at the win - dow, wear - ing the face that she keeps
Look at him work - ing, darn - ing his socks in the night
Fa - ther Mc - Ken - zie, wip - ing the dirt from his hands

To Coda 𝄌

Em6 | **C** | **Em**

in a jar by the door. Who is it for?
when there's no - bo - dy there. What does he care?
as he walks from the grave. No - bo - dy saved.

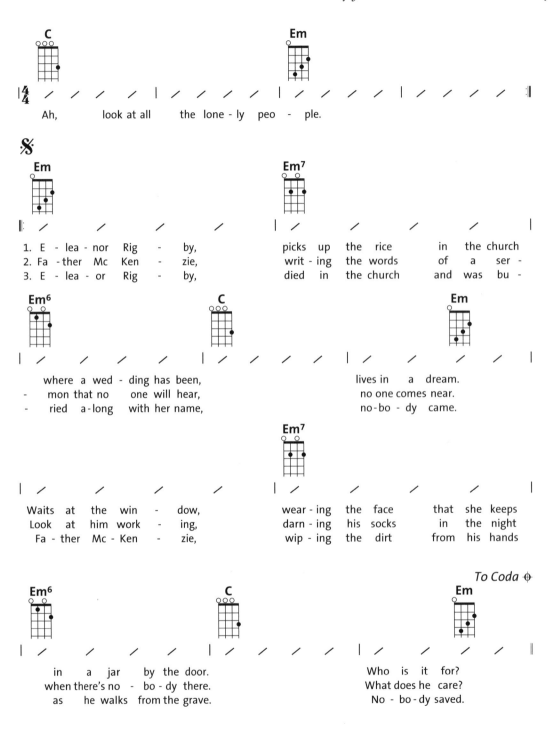

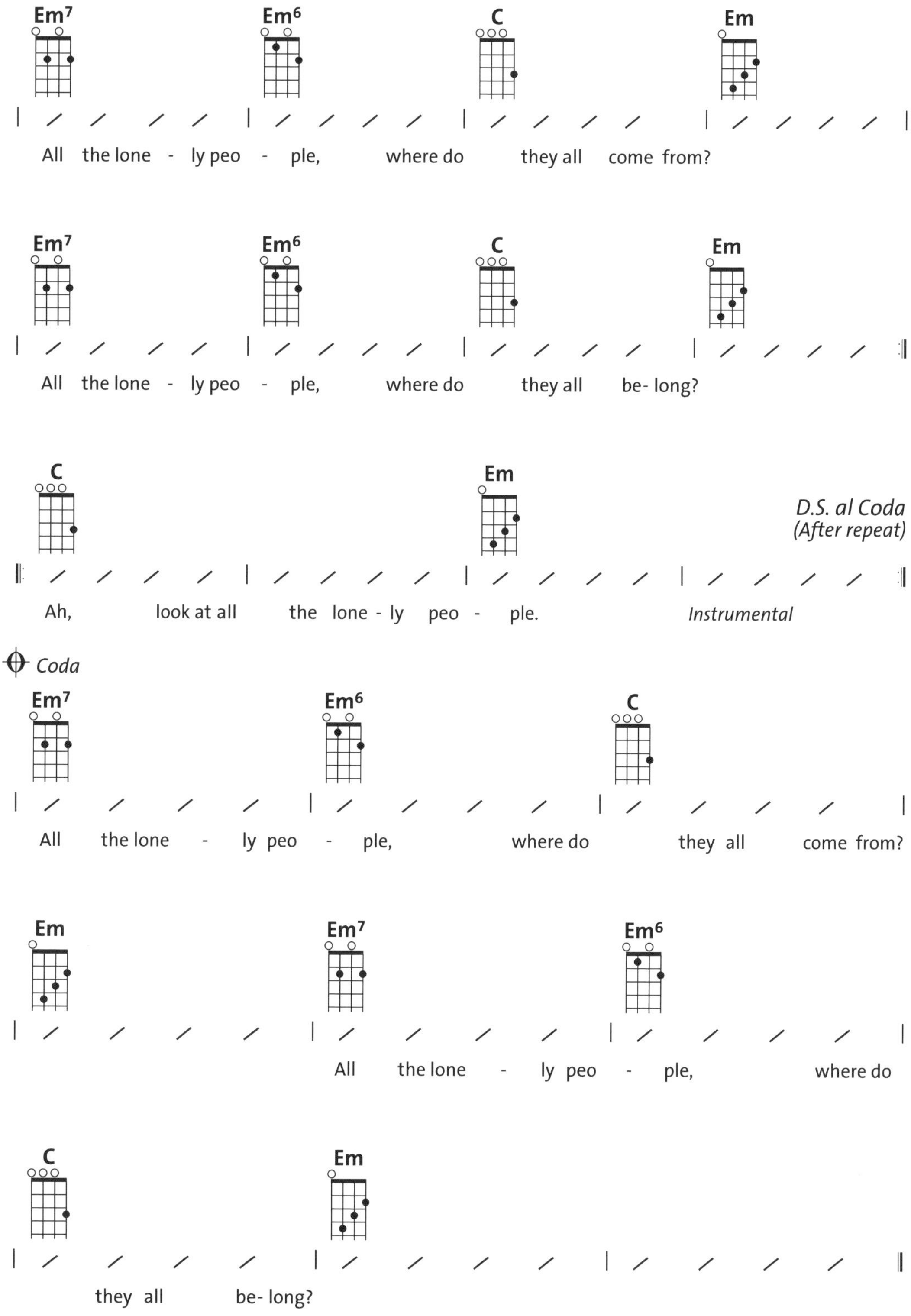
Em7 Em6 C Em
All the lone - ly peo - ple, where do they all come from?
Em7 Em6 C Em
All the lone - ly peo - ple, where do they all be- long?
C Em
D.S. al Coda
(After repeat)
Ah, look at all the lone - ly peo - ple.
Instrumental
Coda
Em7 Em6 C
All the lone - ly peo - ple, where do they all come from?
Em Em7 Em6
All the lone - ly peo - ple, where do
C Em
they all be- long?

from me to you

Words & Music by John Lennon & Paul McCartney

4/4

C | Am | C

Da da da da da dum dum da. Da da da da da dum dum

Am | C | Am

da. 1. If there's an - y-thing that you want, if there's

C | G7 | F7

an - y-thing I can do, just call on me and I'll

Am | C G | C Am

send it a-long, with love from me to you. 2. I've got

C | Am | C | G7

ev-'ry-thing that you want, like a heart that's oh so true. (2. 4.) Just

4. Instrumental (4 bars)

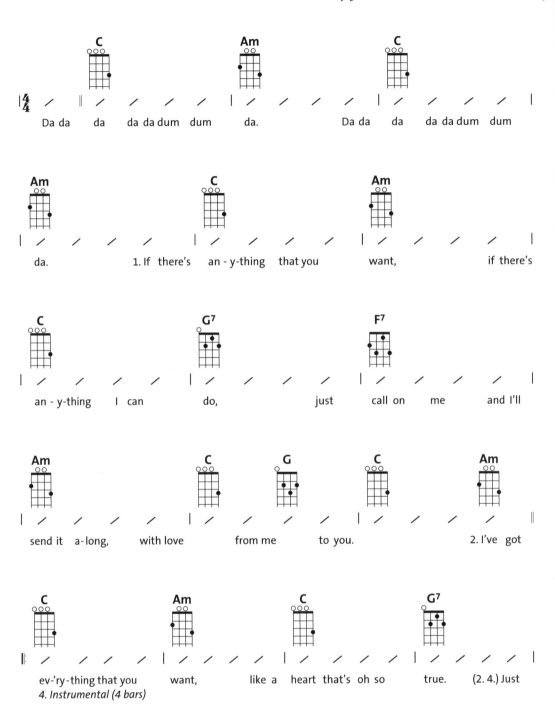

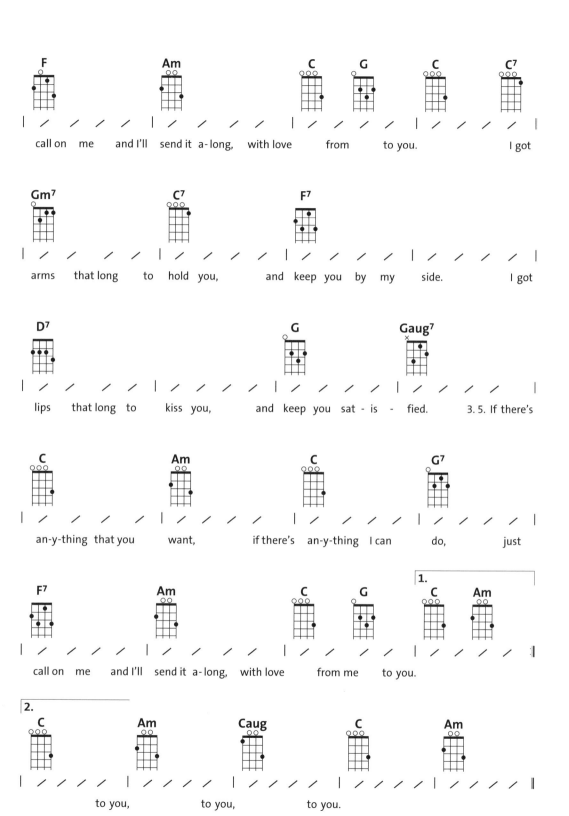

call on me and I'll send it a-long, with love from to you. I got

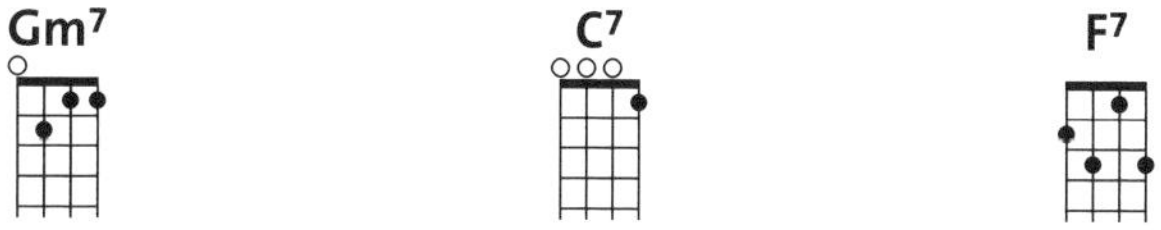

arms that long to hold you, and keep you by my side. I got

lips that long to kiss you, and keep you sat - is - fied. 3. 5. If there's

an-y-thing that you want, if there's an-y-thing I can do, just

1.

call on me and I'll send it a-long, with love from me to you.

2.

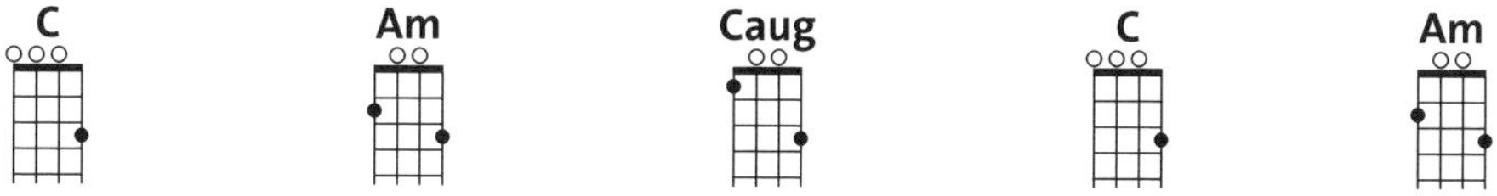

to you, to you, to you.

get back

Words & Music by John Lennon & Paul McCartney

A
G D
2fr
A
A7
1. Jo - jo was a man who thought he was a lo - ner, but
2. Sweet Lo - ret - ta Mar - tin thought she was a wo - man, but
D
A
he knew it could-n't last Jo - jo left his home in Tu -
she was an-oth - er man. All the girls a-round her say
A7
D
A
- cson, A - riz - o - na for some Ca - li - for - nia grass. Get back,
she's got it com-ing, but she gets it while she can.
A7
D
A G D
get back, get back to where you once be-longed. Get back,
A7
D
A
get back, get back to where you once be-longed. Get back, Jo-jo.

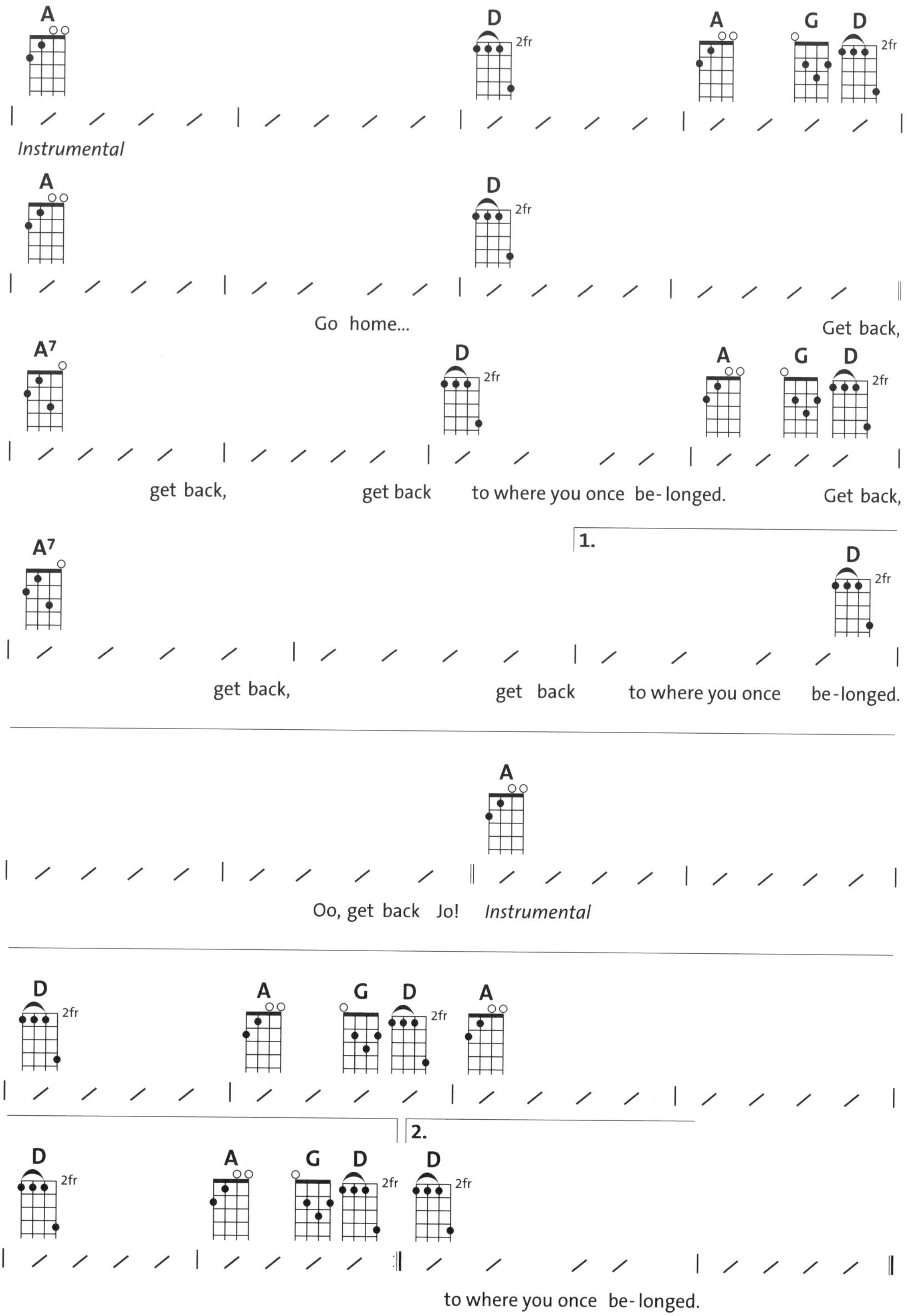
A D A G D
Instrumental
A D
Go home...
Get back,
A7 D A G D
get back,
get back
to where you once be-longed.
Get back,
A7
1.
D
get back,
get back
to where you once
be-longed.
A
Oo, get back Jo!
Instrumental
D A G D A
D A G D
2.
D
to where you once be-longed.

help!

Words & Music by John Lennon & Paul McCartney

Bm **Bm7** **G** **Gmaj7**

Help! I need some bo - dy. Help! Not just a-ny - bo - dy.

E **A**

Help! You know I need some-one, help!

A **C♯m** (4fr)

1. 3. When I was young - er, so much young - er than to - day,
2. And now my life has changed in oh so ma - ny ways,

F♯m **D** (2fr) **G** **A**

I nev-er need - ed a - ny - bo - dy's help in a - ny way.
my in - de - pen - dence seems to va - nish in the haze.

C♯m (4fr)

But now these days are gone I'm not so self - as - sured,
But ev - 'ry now and then I feel so in - se - cure,

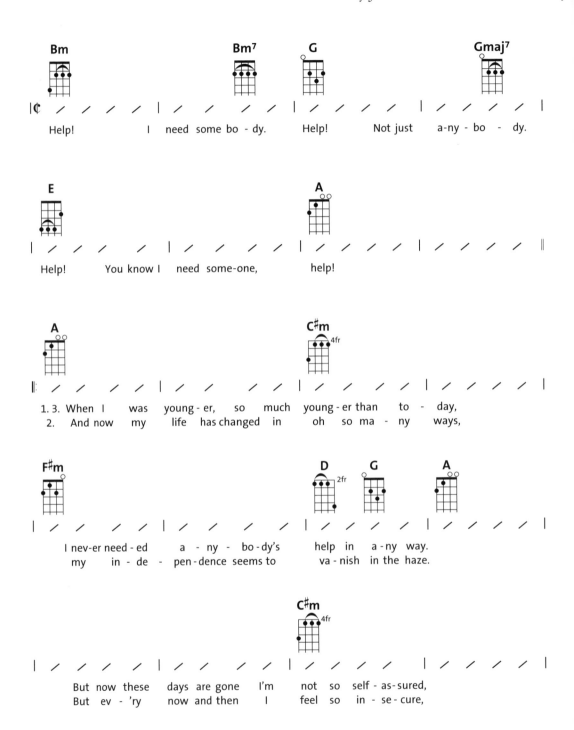

F♯m D G A

now I find I've changed my mind, I've o - pened up the doors.
I know that I just need you like I've nev - er done be - fore.

Bm Bm7

Help me if you can, I'm feel - ing down, and I do

G Gmaj7

ap - pre - ci - ate you be-ing 'round.

E

Help me get my feet back on the ground, won't you

A

1, 2.

please, please help me.

3.

F♯m A A6

Help me, help me, oo.

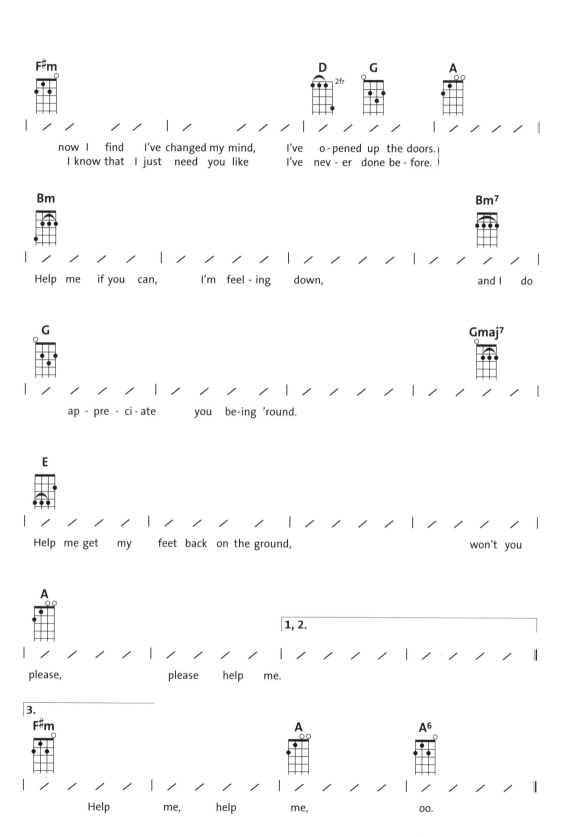

here, there and everywhere

Words & Music by John Lennon & Paul McCartney

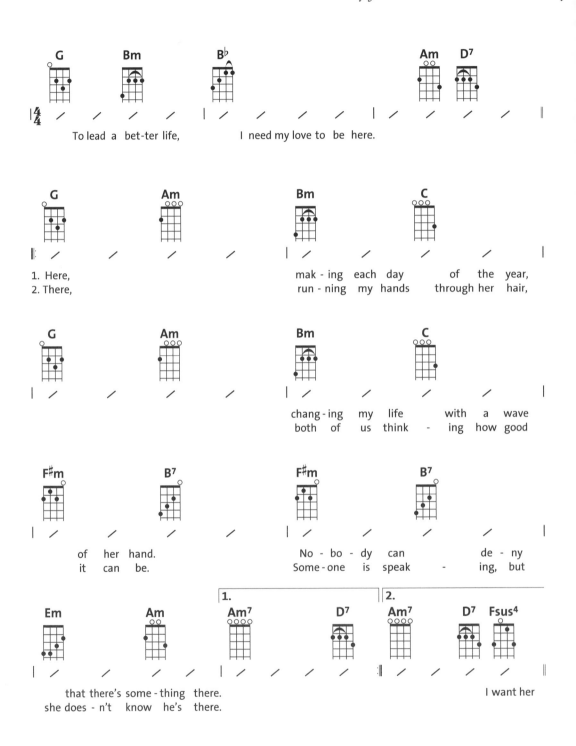

To lead a bet-ter life, I need my love to be here.

1. Here,
2. There,

mak - ing each day of the year,
run - ning my hands through her hair,

chang - ing my life with a wave
both of us think - ing how good

of her hand.
it can be.

No - bo - dy can de - ny
Some - one is speak - ing, but

that there's some - thing there.
she does - n't know he's there.

I want her

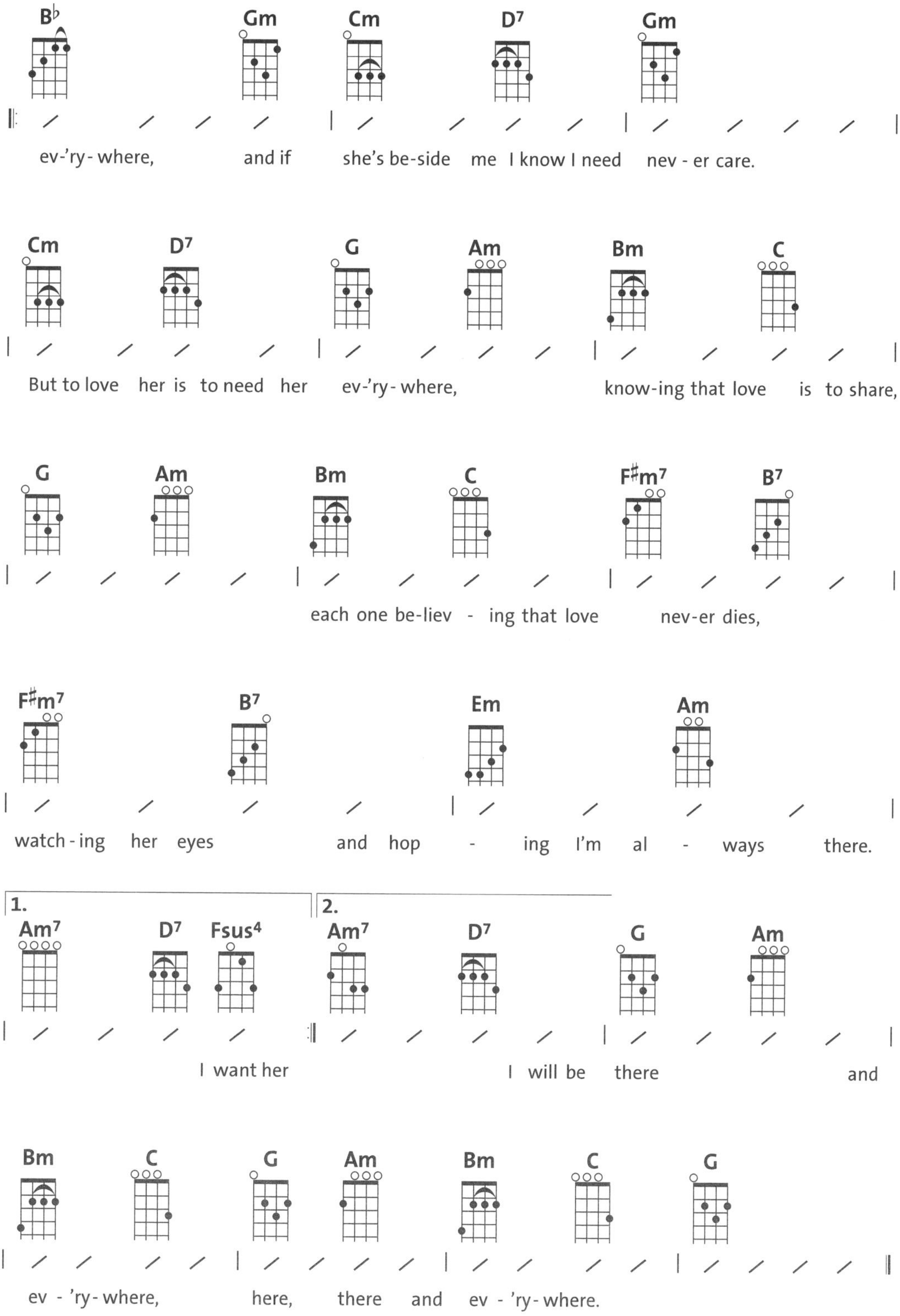
B♭ Gm Cm D7 Gm
ev-'ry-where, and if she's be-side me I know I need nev-er care.
Cm D7 G Am Bm C
But to love her is to need her ev-'ry-where, know-ing that love is to share,
G Am Bm C F♯m7 B7
each one be-liev-ing that love nev-er dies,
F♯m7 B7 Em Am
watch-ing her eyes and hop-ing I'm al-ways there.
1. Am7 D7 Fsus4
I want her
2. Am7 D7 G Am
I will be there and
Bm C G Am Bm C G
ev-'ry-where, here, there and ev-'ry-where.

i want to hold your hand

Words & Music by John Lennon & Paul McCartney

D 2fr | C | D 2fr | C | D 2fr

4/4 / / | / / / / | / / / / | / / / / | / / / / ||

1. Oh yeah,

𝄋 G | D 2fr | Em

(1.) I'll tell you some - thing I think you'll un - der -
(2.) please say to me and let me be your
(3. 4.) you got that some - thing I think you'll un - der -

B7 | G | D 2fr

- stand. When I say that some - thing,
man. And please say to me
- stand. When I say that some - thing,

Em | B7 | C D 2fr

I want to hold your hand, I want to hold your
you'll let me hold your hand, now let me hold your
I want to hold your hand, I want to hold your

G Em *To Coda* ⊕ | C D 2fr | 1. G

hand, I want to hold your hand. 2. Oh,
hand, I want to hold your
hand,

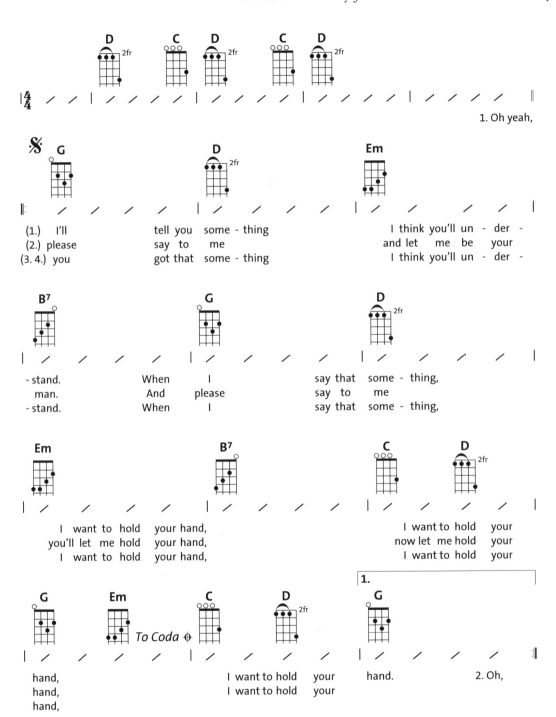

2, 3.

G | **Dm** | **G**

hand. And when I touch you I feel

C | **Am** | **Dm**

hap - py in - side, it's such a

G | **C** **D** | **C** **D**

feel - ing that, my love, I can't hide, I can't hide,

C **D**

I can't hide.

D.S. (twice)
2° al Coda

3. 4. Yeah,

Coda

C **D** | **B7**

I want to hold your hand,

C **D** | **C** | **G**

I want to hold your hand.

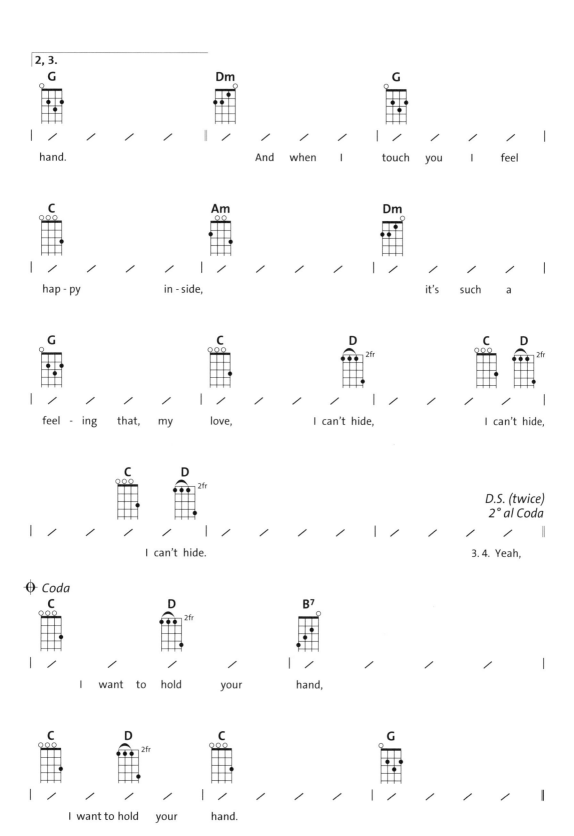

in my life

Words & Music by John Lennon & Paul McCartney

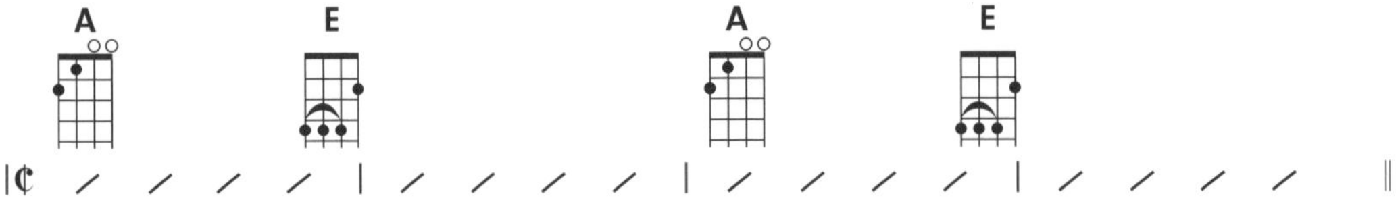

Instrumental 1. There are

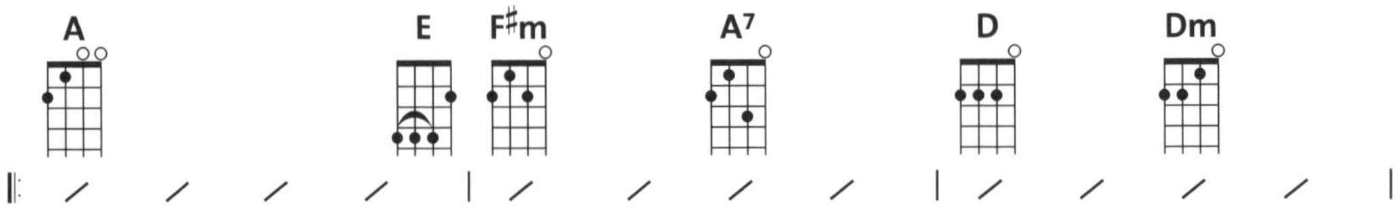

(1.) pla - ces I re - mem-ber all my life, though
(2.) all these friend and lov - ers, there is no one com -

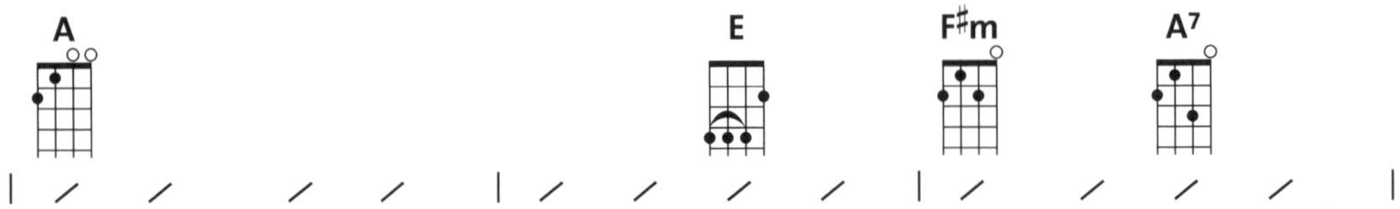

some have changed. Some for ev - er, not for bet - ter; some have
-pares with you. And these mem - 'ries lose their mean-ing, when I

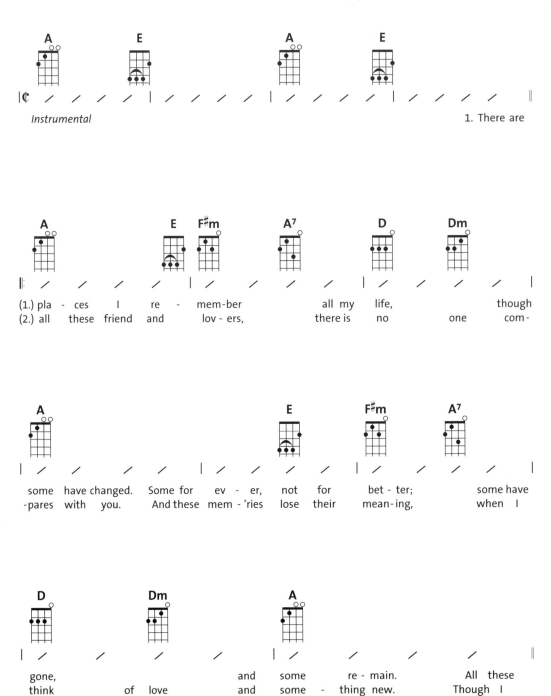

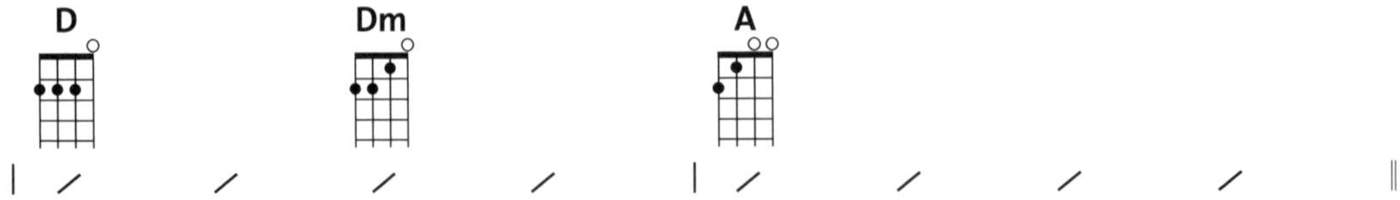

gone, and some re - main. All these
think of love and some - thing new. Though I

F♯m | D

pla - ces had their mo-ments, with
know I'll nev - er lose af - fec - tion for

G | A

lov - ers and friends, I still can re - call. Some are
peo - ple and things that went be - fore. I

F♯m | D | Dm

dead and some are liv - ing: in my life, I've
know I'll of-ten stop to think a - bout them; in my life, I'll

A

loved them all.
love you more.

1. E

Instrumental 2. But of

2. A E | Dm

Instrumental In my life, I'll

N.C. 2/4 | 4/4 A | E | A

love you more.

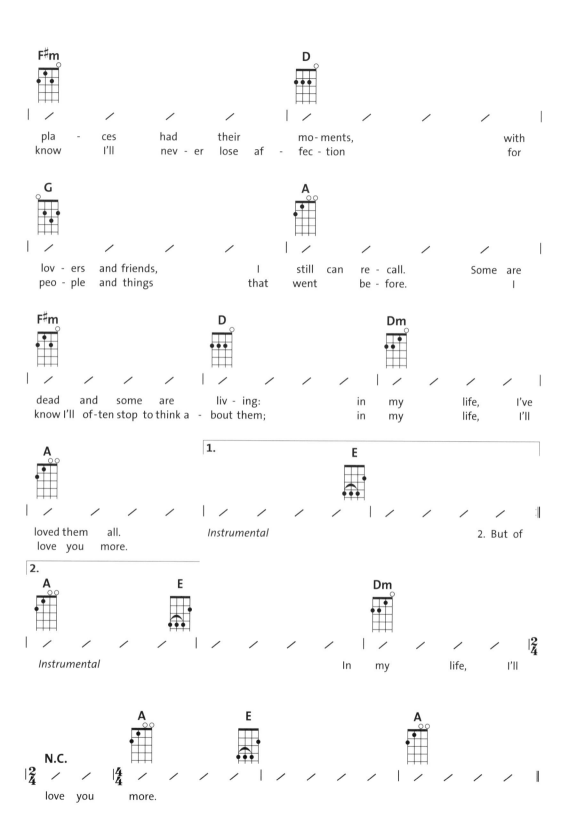

can't buy me love

Words & Music by John Lennon & Paul McCartney

N.C. | Em | Am | Em

Can't buy me love, love,

Am | Dm7 | G7

can't buy me love. 1. I'll

C7

buy you a dia - mond ring my friend if it makes you feel all right.
give you all I've got to give if you say you love me too.

F7

I'll get you an - y - thing my friend if it
I may not have a lot to give but what I

C7 | G

makes you feel all right. 'Cause I don't care too
got I'll give to you. I don't care too

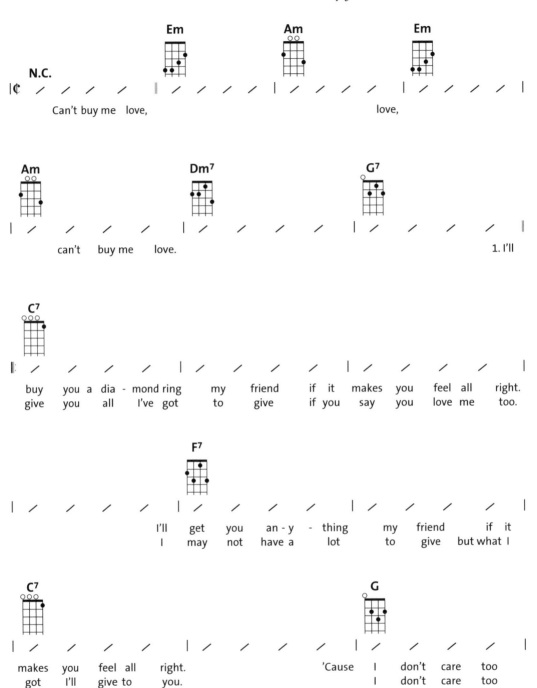

F7 | 1. C

much for mon-ey, mon-ey can't buy me love.
much for mon-ey, mon-ey can't buy me love. 2. I'll

2. C | 𝄋 Em | Am

Can't buy me love, ev -

C | Em

- 'ry-bod-y tells me so. Can't buy me love,

Am | Dm7 | G7 | C7

no no no no. 3. 4. Say you don't need no

F7

dia-mond rings, and I'll be sat-is - fied. Tell me that you want the

C7 | G

kind of things that mon-ey just can't buy. I don't care too

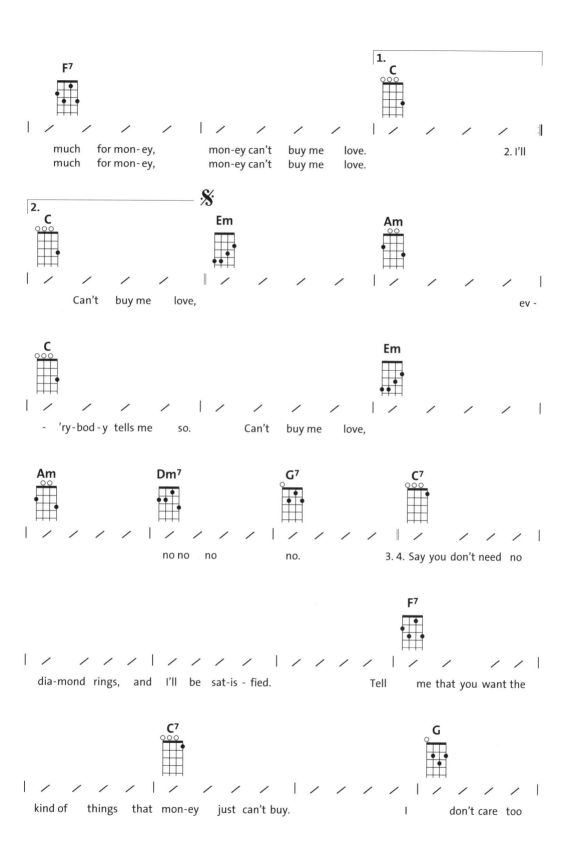

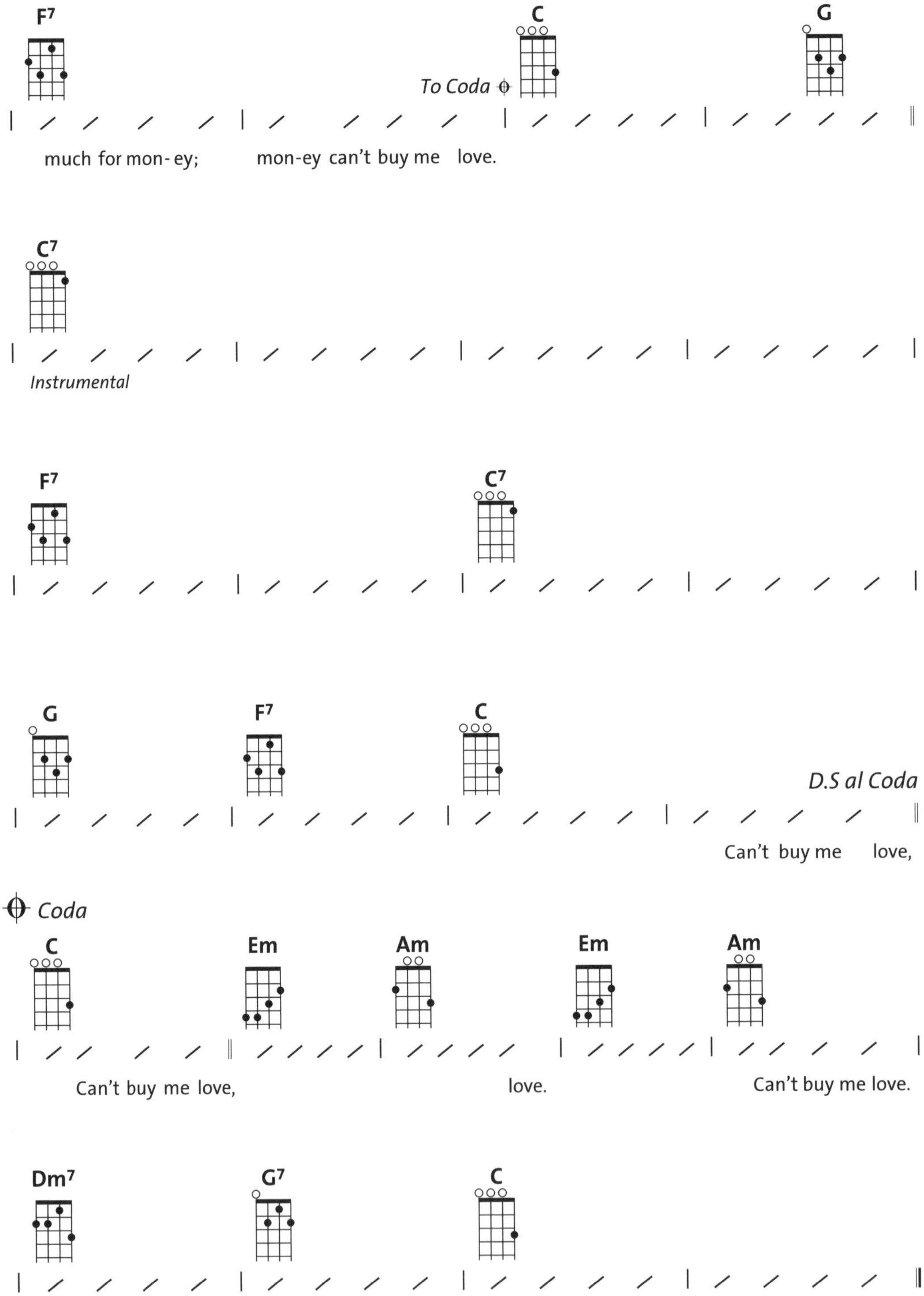

much for mon- ey;   mon-ey can't buy me love.

Instrumental

D.S al Coda

Can't buy me   love,

⊕ *Coda*

Can't buy me love,   love.   Can't buy me love.

lady madonna

Words & Music by John Lennon & Paul McCartney

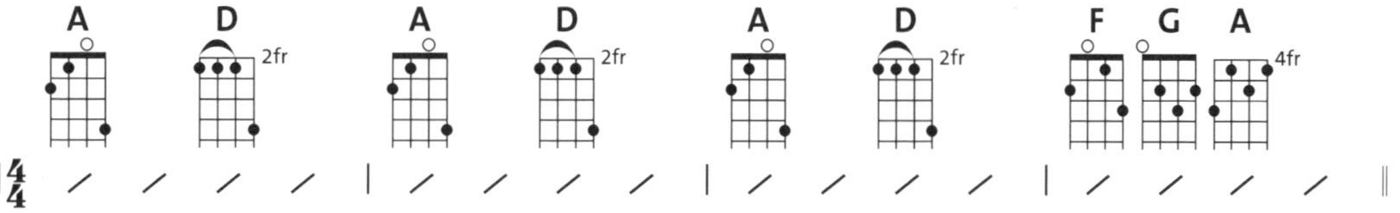

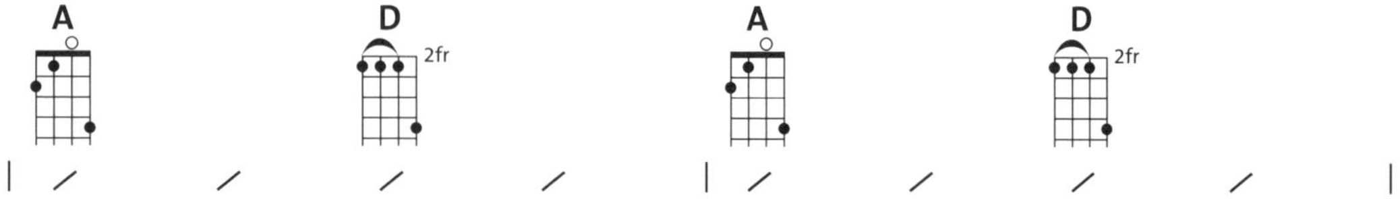

La - dy Mad - on - na,______ child - ren at your feet,

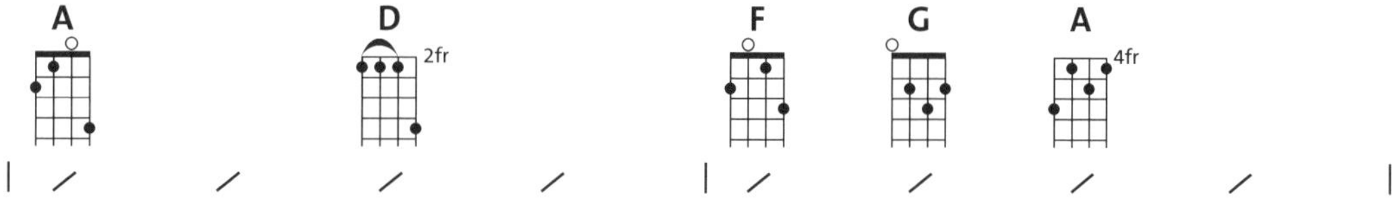

won - der how you man - age to make ends meet.

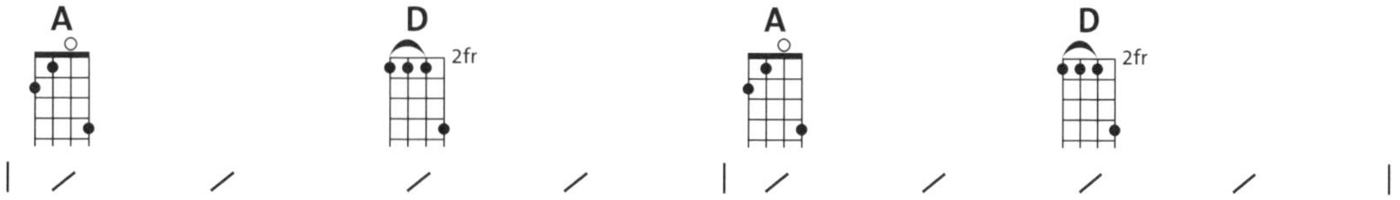

Who finds the mon - ey, when you pay the rent?

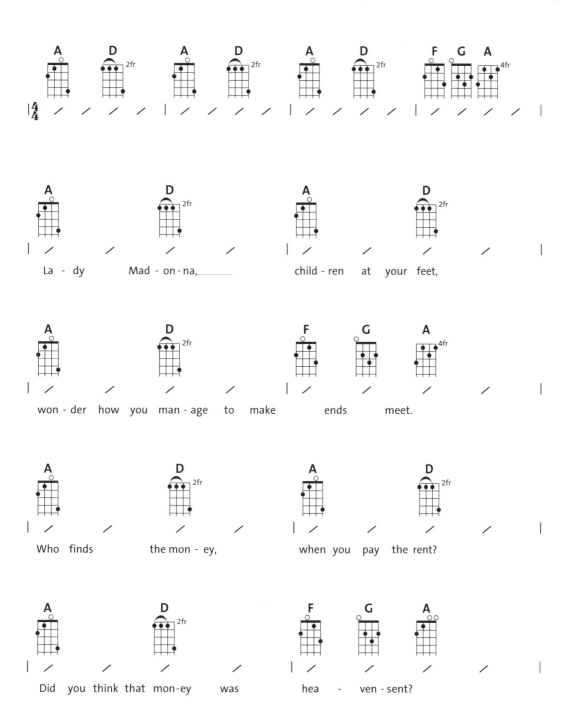

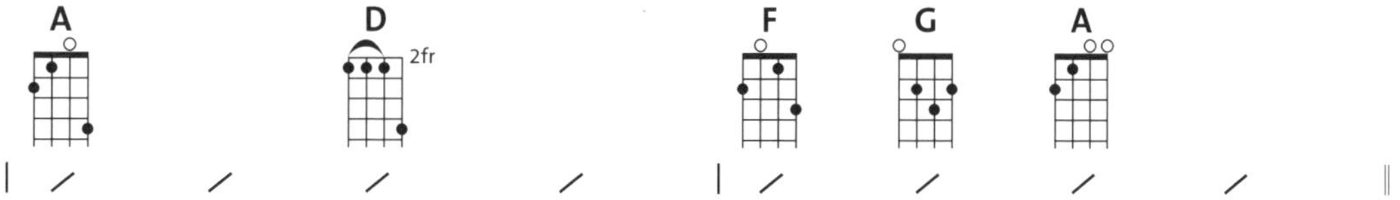

Did you think that mon-ey was hea - ven - sent?

Dm⁷ **G⁷**

1. Fri - day night ar - rives with - out_ a suit - case,
2. *Instrumental*
3. Tues - day af - ter - noon is nev - er end - ing,

C **Am⁷**

Sun - day morn - ing creep - ing like a nun.

Wed - nesday morn - ing pa - pers did - n't come.

Dm⁷ **G⁷**

Mon - day's child has learned to tie his boot - lace.

Thurs - day night your stock - ings need - ed mend - ing.

C **Bm⁷** **E⁷sus⁴** **E⁷**

See how they run.
See how they run.
See how they run.

A **D** **A** **D**

La - dy Ma - don - na, ba - by at your breast,
La - dy Ma - don - na, ly - ing on the bed,
La - dy Ma - don - na, child - ren at your feet,

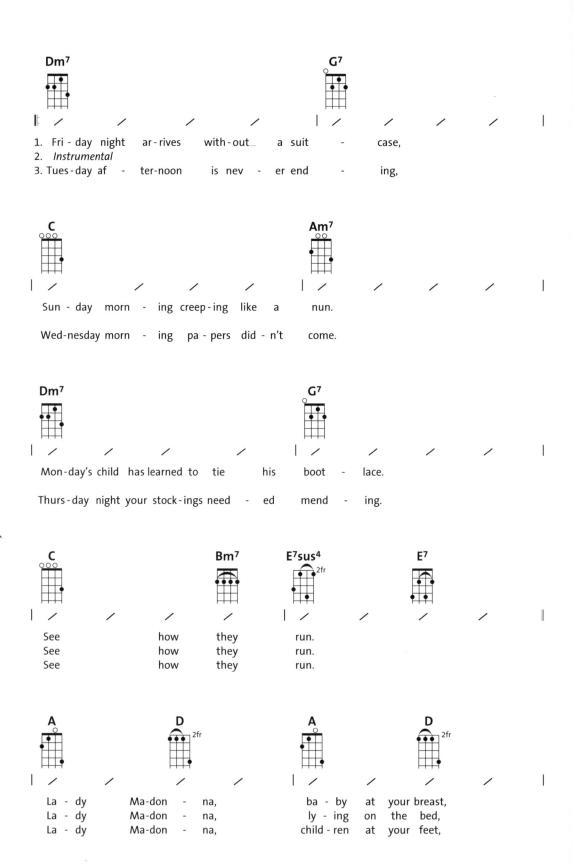

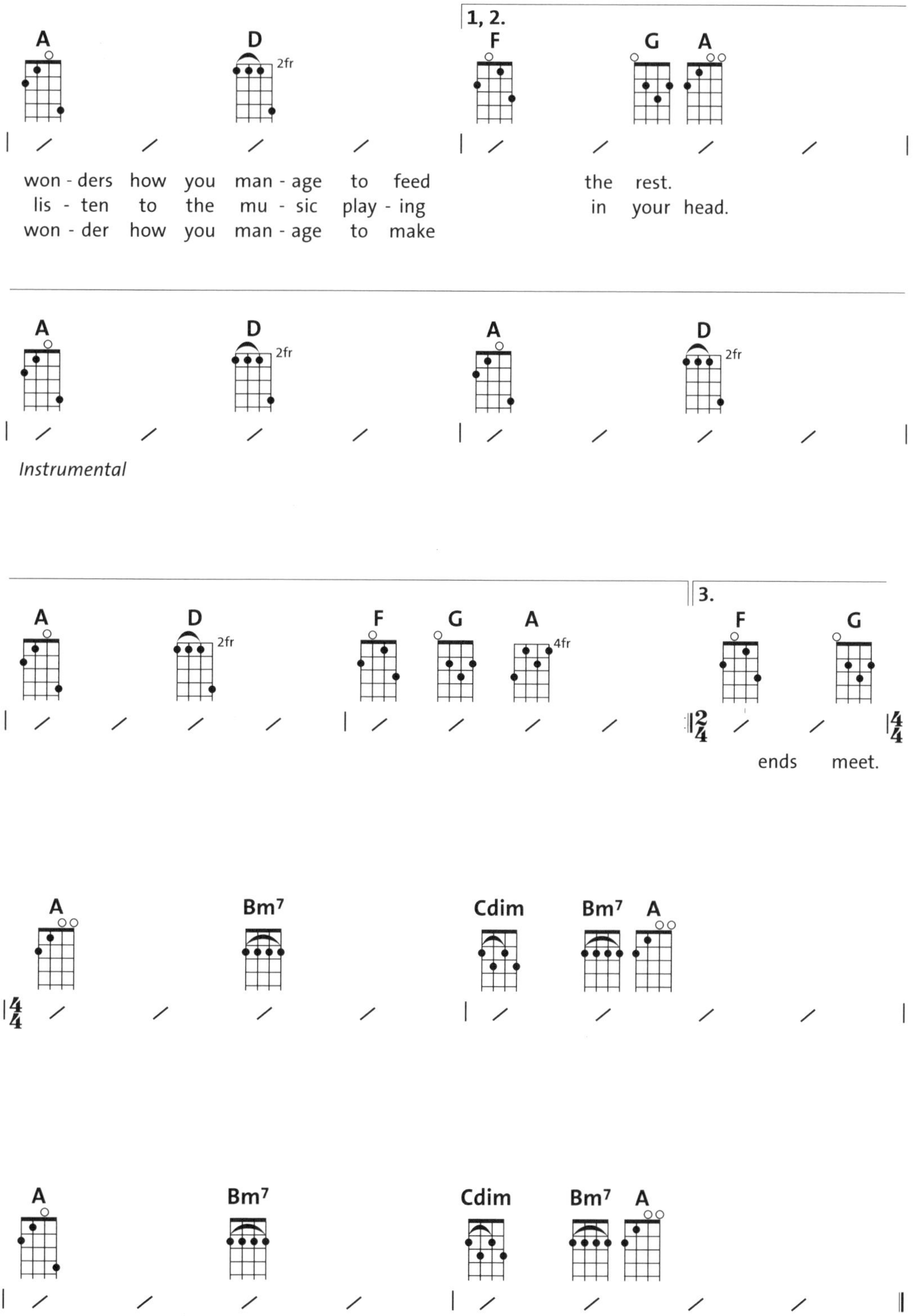
1, 2.
A
D
2fr
F
G
A
won - ders how you man - age to feed
lis - ten to the mu - sic play - ing
won - der how you man - age to make
the rest.
in your head.
A
D
2fr
A
D
2fr
Instrumental
A
D
2fr
F
G
A
4fr
3.
F
G
ends meet.
A
Bm7
Cdim
Bm7
A
A
Bm7
Cdim
Bm7
A

lucy in the sky with diamonds

Words & Music by John Lennon & Paul McCartney

3/4

A	A/G	F♯m
/ / /	/ / /	/ / /
1. Pic - ture your -	self in a	boat on a
2. Fol - low her	down to a	bridge by a
3. Pic - ture your -	self on a	train by a

Dm	A	A/G	F♯m
/ / /	/ / /	/ / /	/ / /
riv - er, with	tan - ger - ine	trees and	mar - ma - lade
foun - tain, where	rock - ing horse	peo - ple eat	marsh - mal - low
sta - tion, with	pla - ti - cine	por - ters with	look - ing - glass

Dm		A	A/G
/ / /	/ / /	/ / /	/ / /
skies.		Some - bo - dy	calls you, you
pies.		Ev - 'ry - one	smiles as you
ties.		Sud - den - ly	some - one is

F♯m	Dm	A	A/G
/ / /	/ / /	/ / /	/ / /
ans - wer quite	slow - ly,	a girl with	ka - lei - do - scope
drift past the	flow - ers	that grow so	in - cre - di - bly
there at the	turn - stile,	the girl with	ka - lei - do - scope

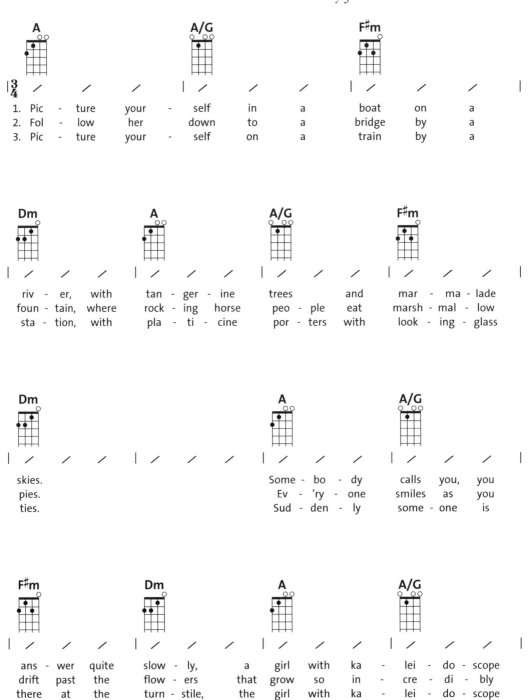

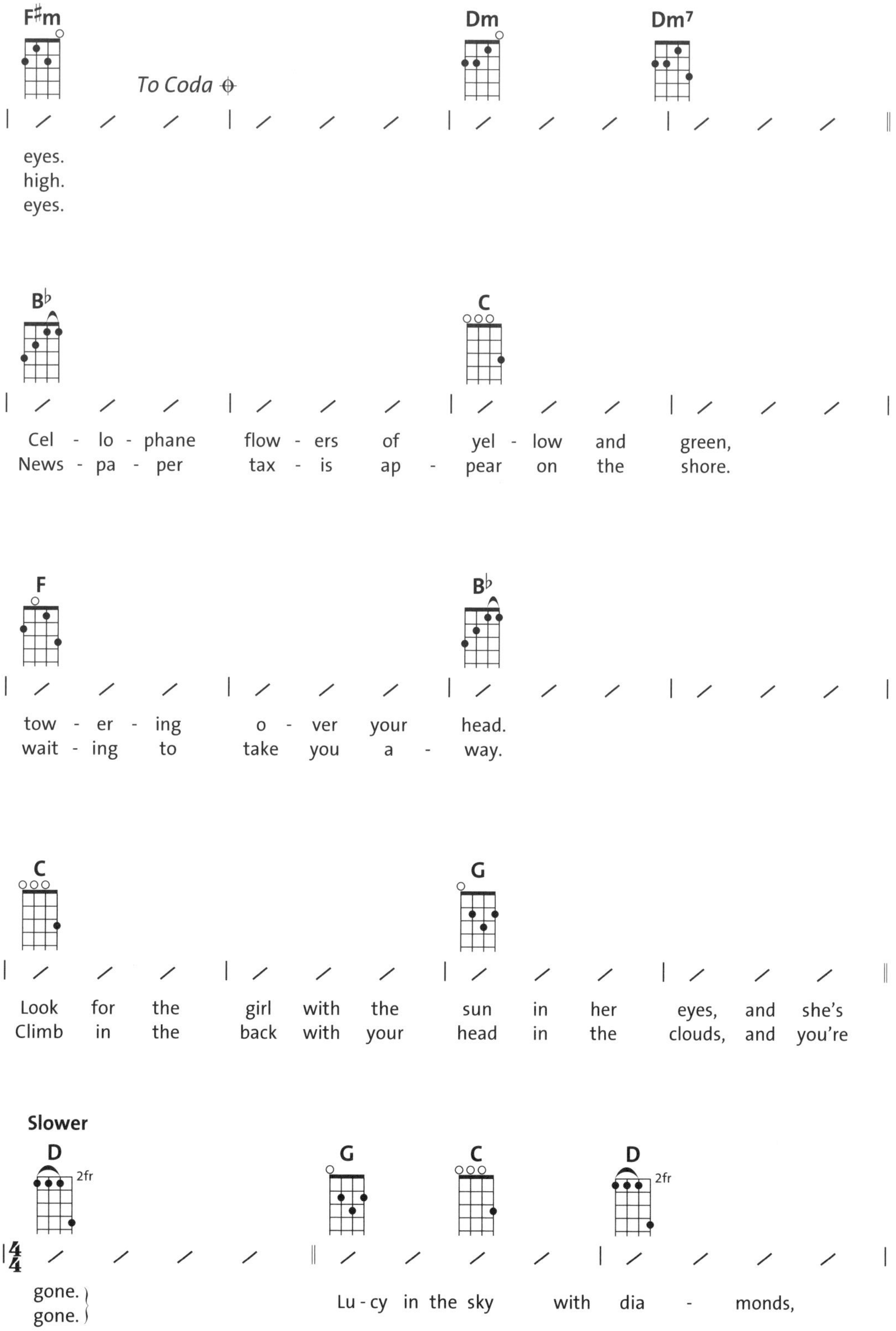
F♯m
To Coda
Dm
Dm7
eyes.
high.
eyes.
B♭
C
Cel - lo - phane flow - ers of yel - low and green,
News - pa - per tax - is ap - pear on the shore.
F
B♭
tow - er - ing o - ver your head.
wait - ing to take you a - way.
C
G
Look for the girl with the sun in her eyes, and she's
Climb in the back with your head in the clouds, and you're
Slower
D
2fr
G
C
D
2fr
4
4
gone.
gone.
Lu - cy in the sky with dia - monds,

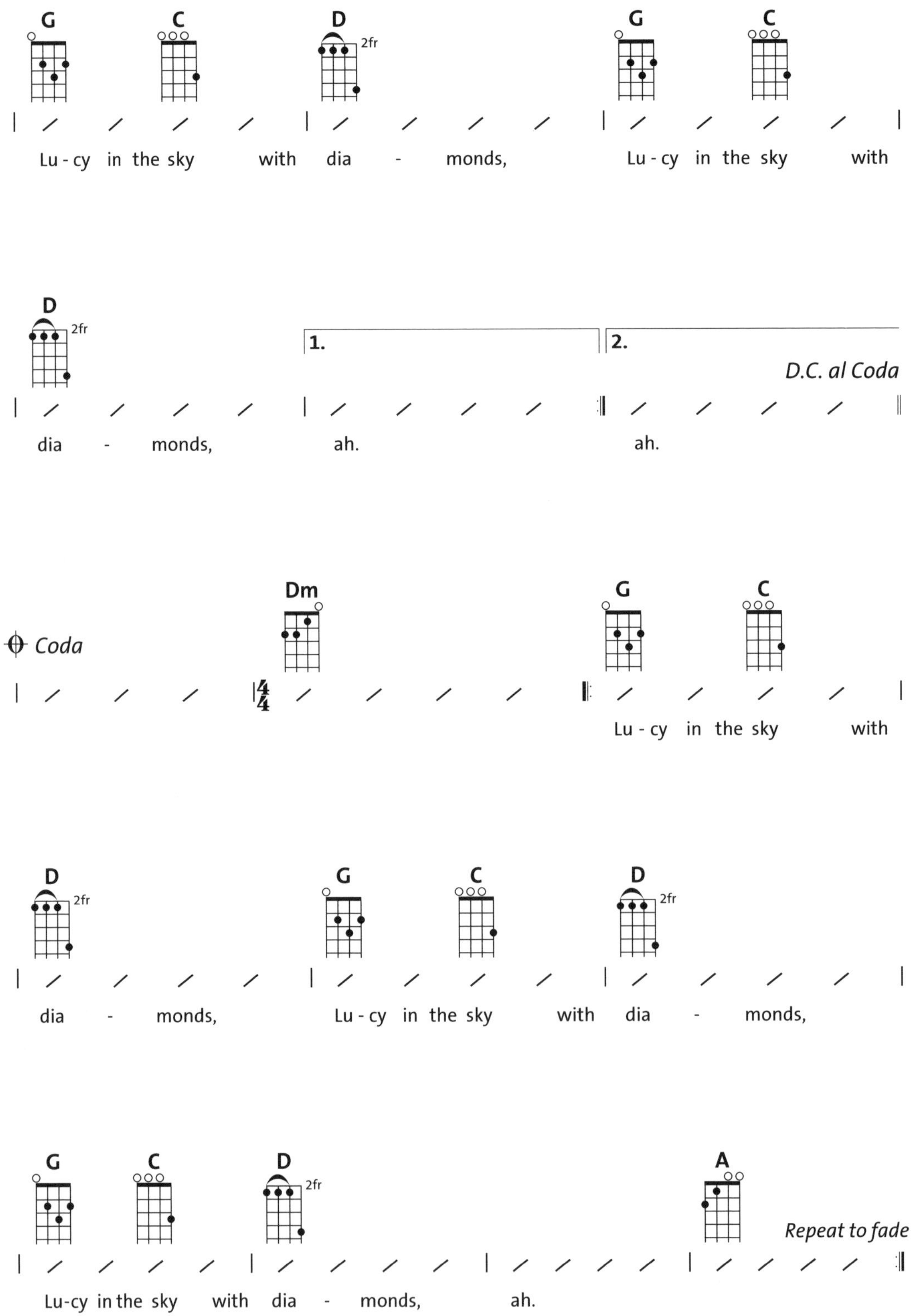
G C D 2fr G C
Lu - cy in the sky with dia - monds, Lu - cy in the sky with
D 2fr
1. 2.
D.C. al Coda
dia - monds, ah. ah.
Coda
Dm G C
4/4
Lu - cy in the sky with
D 2fr G C D 2fr
dia - monds, Lu - cy in the sky with dia - monds,
G C D 2fr A
Repeat to fade
Lu-cy in the sky with dia - monds, ah.

michelle

Words & Music by John Lennon & Paul McCartney

Fm | Fm/E | Fm/E♭ | Fm/D | B♭m7 | C7

F | B♭m7 | E♭

Mi - chelle, ma belle, these are words that

Ddim | C | Ddim | C7

go to - geth - er well, my Mi-chelle.

F | B♭m7 | E♭

1. Mi - chelle, ma belle, sont les mots qui
2. Mi - chelle, ma belle, sont les mots qui

Ddim | C | Ddim | C7

vont très bien en - semble, très bien en - semble.
vont très bien en - semble, très bien en - semble.

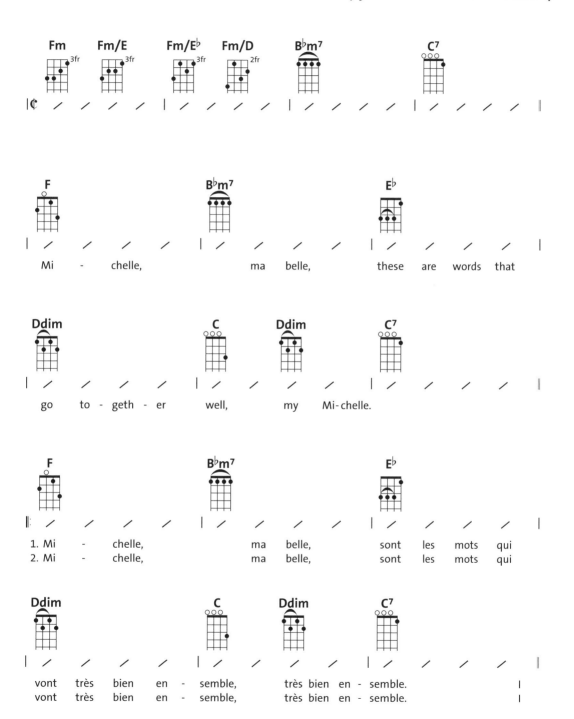

𝄋

Fm (3fr) | **A♭sus4**

love you, I love you, I love you. That's all I want to say.
need to, I need to, I need to. I need to make you see.
𝄋 want you, I want you, I want you. I think you know by now.

D♭maj7 | **C7** | **Fm** (3fr)

Un - til I find a way. I will
Oh what you mean to me. Un -
I'll get to you some- how. Un -

Fm (3fr) **Fm/E** (3fr) | **Fm/E♭** (3fr) **Fm/D** (2fr) | **D♭maj7**

say the on - ly words I know that you'll un - der -
- til I do I'm hop - ing you will know what I
- til I do I'm tell - ing you so you'll un - der -

C7 *To Coda* 𝄌 | **F** | **B♭m7**

- stand. I love you.
mean.
- stand.

E♭ | **Ddim** | **C** **Ddim** | **C7** *D.S. al Coda (no repeat)*

I

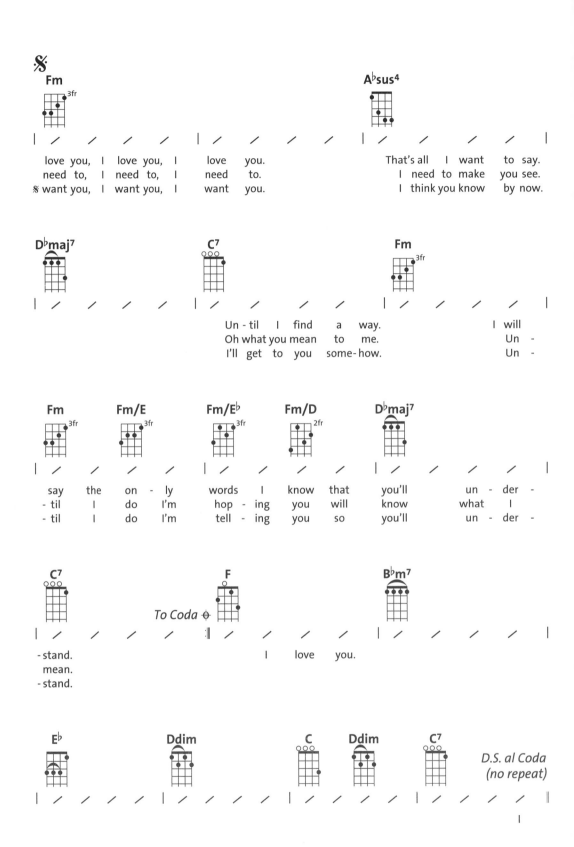

Coda

F | Bbm7 | Eb | Ddim

4. Mi - chelle, ma belle. sont les mots qui vont très bien en -

C | Ddim | C7 | Fm | Fm/E

-semble, très bien en - semble. And I will say the on - ly

Fm/Eb | Fm/D | Dbmaj7 | Bbm7 | C7 | Fm | C7

words I know that you'll un - der - stand, my Mi -

F | Bbm7 | Eb

-chelle. *Instrumental*

Ddim | C | Ddim | C7

Repeat to fade

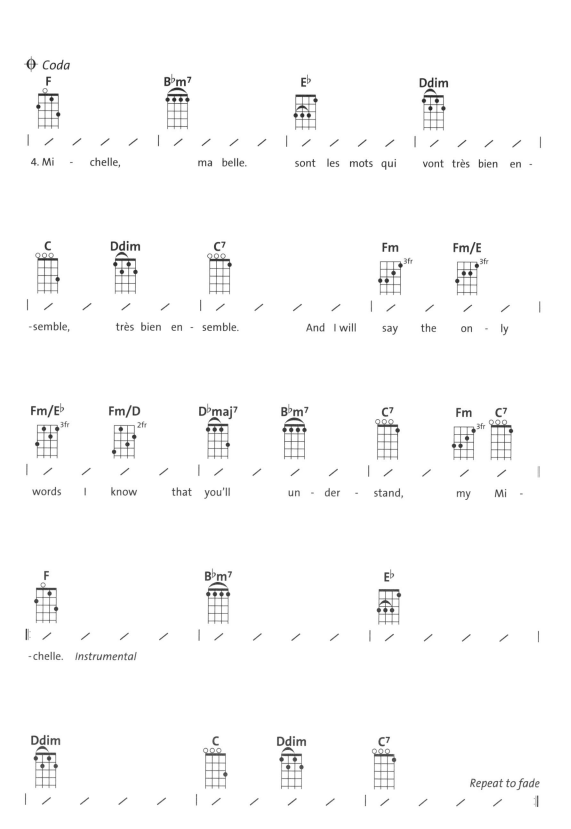

norwegian wood

Words & Music by John Lennon & Paul McCartney

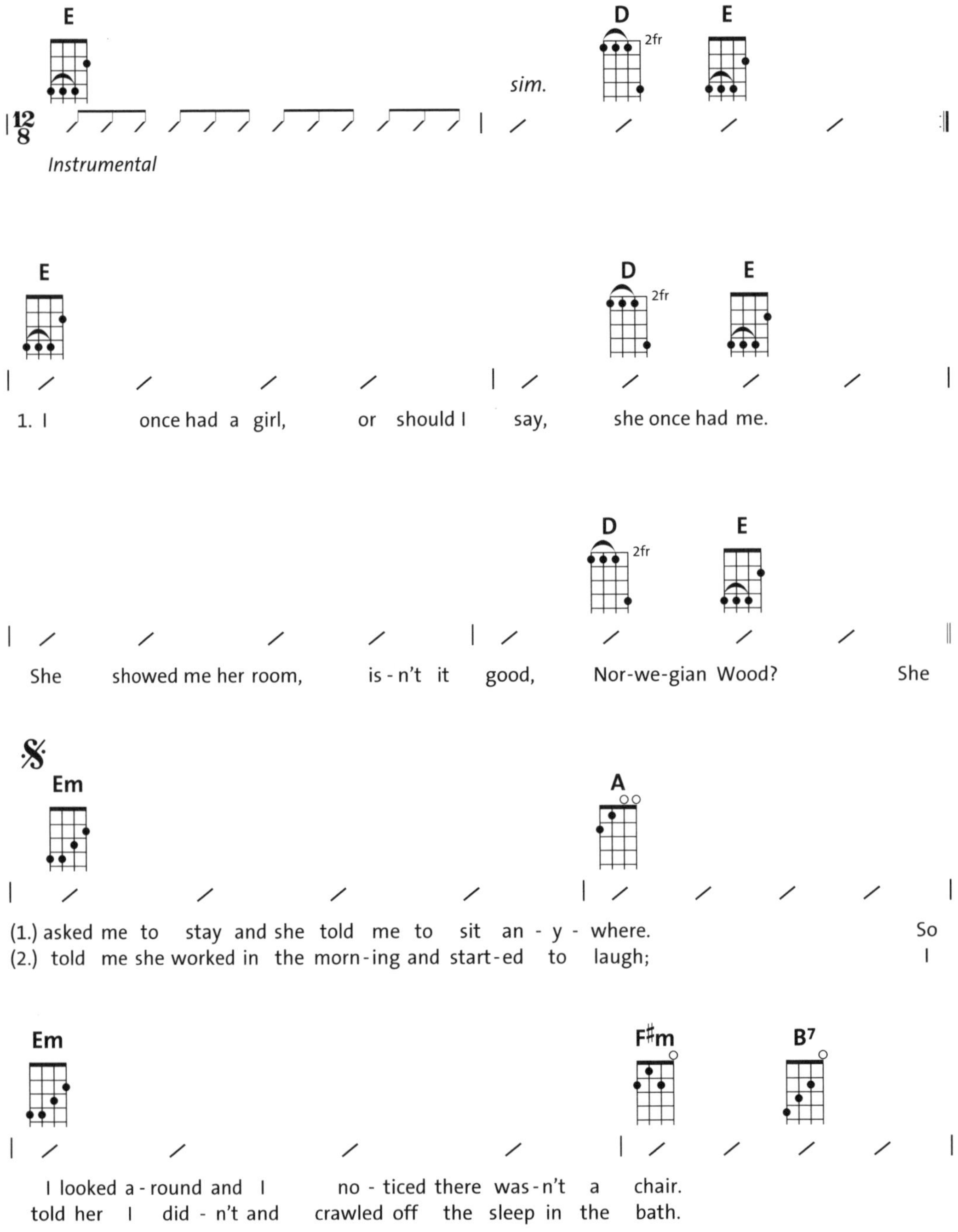
E
D
2fr
E
sim.
12/8
Instrumental
E
D
2fr
E
1. I once had a girl, or should I say, she once had me.
D
2fr
E
She showed me her room, is - n't it good, Nor-we-gian Wood? She
Em
A
(1.) asked me to stay and she told me to sit an - y - where. So
(2.) told me she worked in the morn-ing and start-ed to laugh; I
Em
F♯m
B7
I looked a - round and I no - ticed there was - n't a chair.
told her I did - n't and crawled off the sleep in the bath.

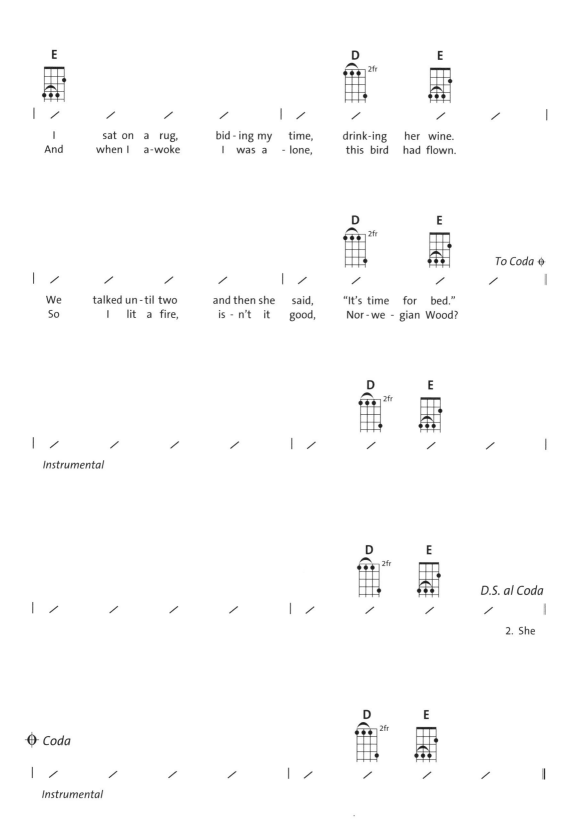

E  D 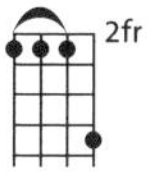 E 

I sat on a rug, bid-ing my time, drink-ing her wine.
And when I a-woke I was a-lone, this bird had flown.

D 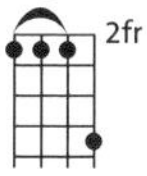 E 

To Coda 𝄌

We talked un-til two and then she said, "It's time for bed."
So I lit a fire, is-n't it good, Nor-we-gian Wood?

D 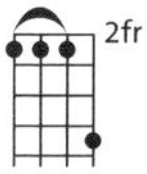 E 

Instrumental

D 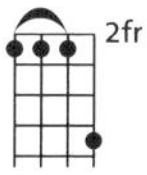 E 

D.S. al Coda

2. She

𝄌 *Coda*

D 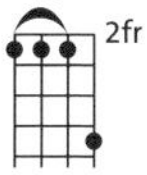 E 

Instrumental

she loves you

Words & Music by John Lennon & Paul McCartney

4/4

Em | A7

She loves you, yeah, yeah, yeah. She loves you, yeah, yeah, yeah. She

C | G6

loves you, yeah, yeah, yeah, yeah! 1. You

𝄋 G | Em7 (3fr) | Bm | D7

(1.) think you've lost your love, well, I saw her yes - ter - day-ee-ay. It's
(2.) said you hurt her so, she al - most lost her mind. But
(3.) know it's up to you, I think it's on - ly fair.

G | Em7 (3fr) | Bm | D7

you she's think-ing of, and she told me what to say-ee-ay.
know she says she knows, you're not the hurt - ing kind.
pride can hurt you too, a - po - lo - gise to her.
She says she

G | Em

loves you, and you know that can't be bad; yes, she

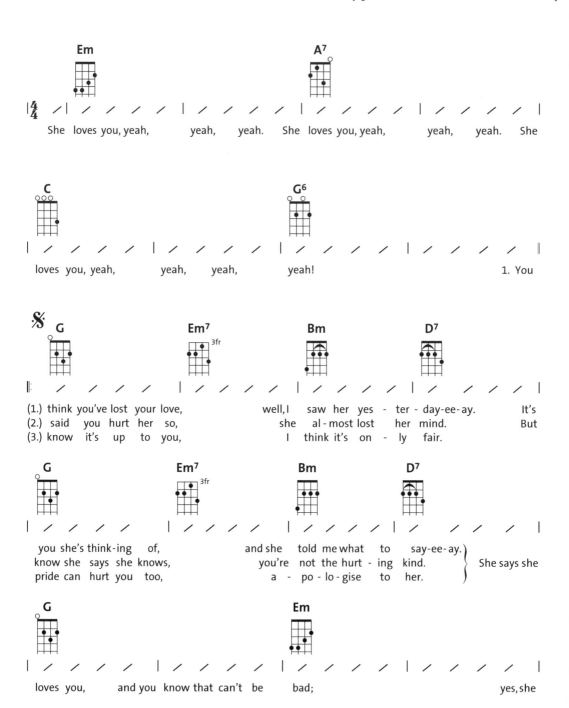

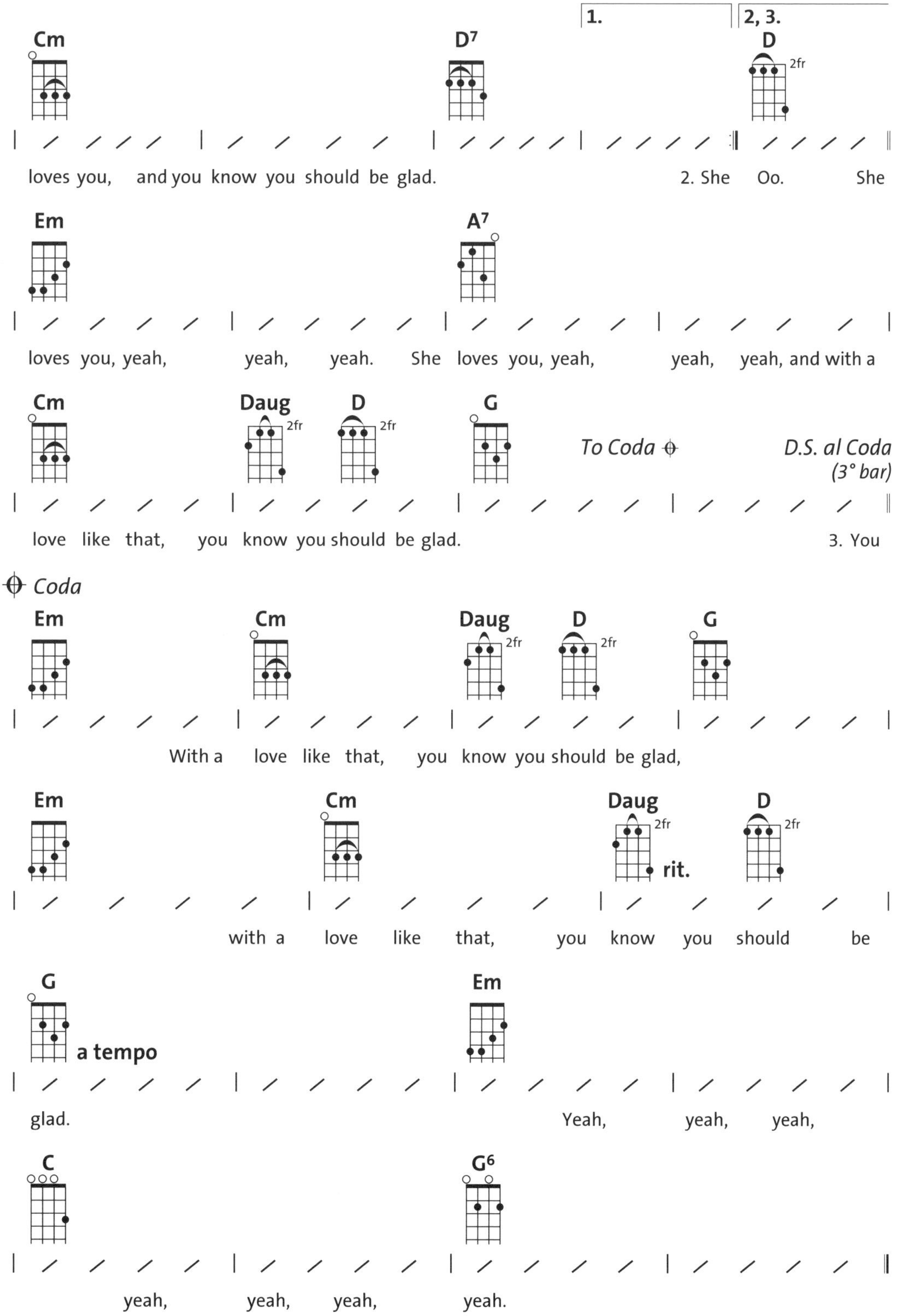
1.
2, 3.
Cm
D7
D 2fr
loves you, and you know you should be glad.
2. She Oo. She
Em
A7
loves you, yeah, yeah, yeah. She loves you, yeah, yeah, yeah, and with a
Cm
Daug 2fr
D 2fr
G
To Coda
D.S. al Coda (3° bar)
love like that, you know you should be glad.
3. You
Coda
Em
Cm
Daug 2fr
D 2fr
G
With a love like that, you know you should be glad,
Em
Cm
Daug 2fr
rit.
D 2fr
with a love like that, you know you should be
G
a tempo
Em
glad.
Yeah, yeah, yeah,
C
G6
yeah, yeah, yeah, yeah.

please please me

Words & Music by John Lennon & Paul McCartney

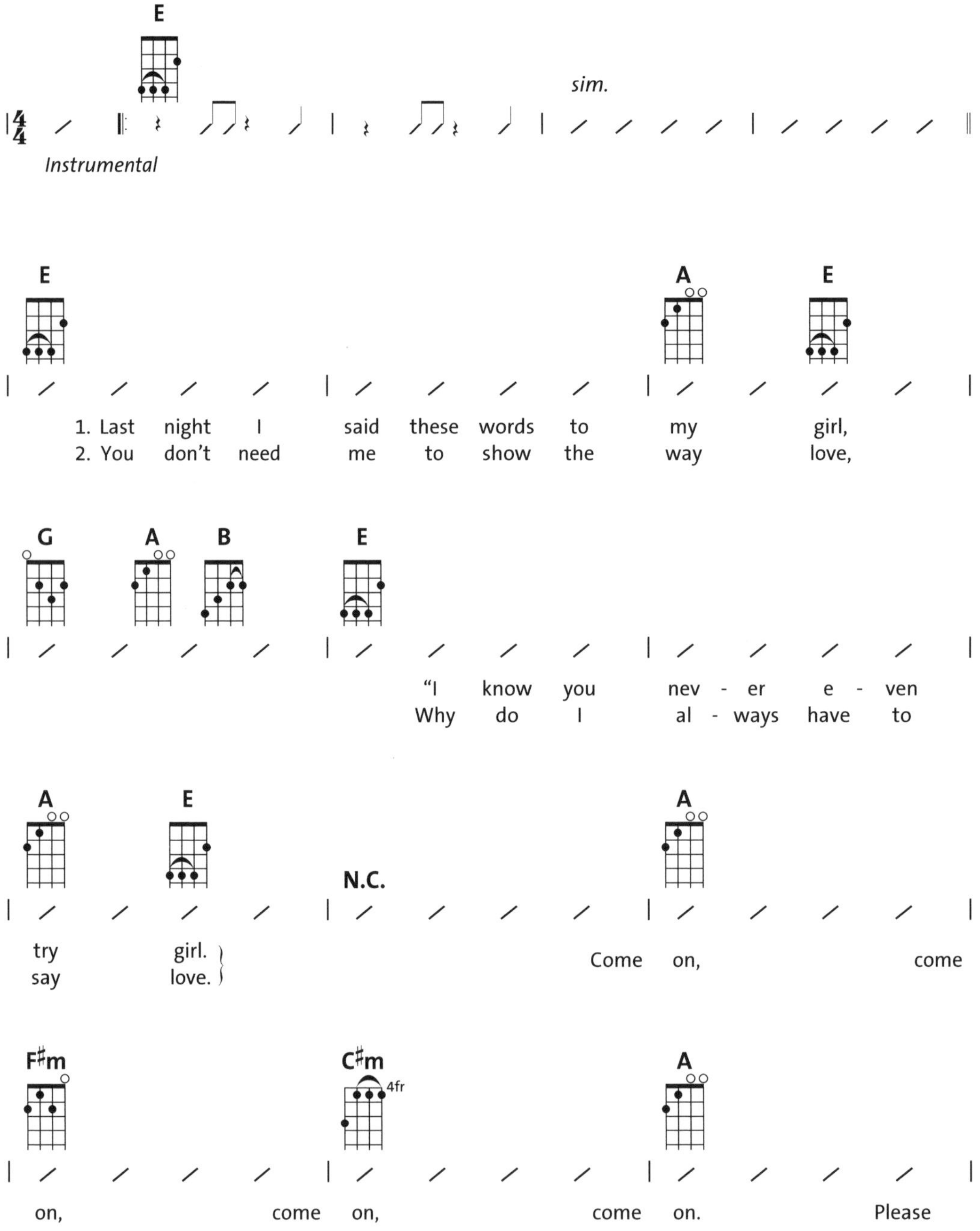
E
sim.
Instrumental
E
A
E
1. Last night I said these words to my girl,
2. You don't need me to show the way love,
G
A
B
E
"I know you nev - er e - ven
Why do I al - ways have to
A
E
N.C.
A
try girl.
say love.
Come on, come
F♯m
C♯m
4fr
A
on, come on, come on.
Please

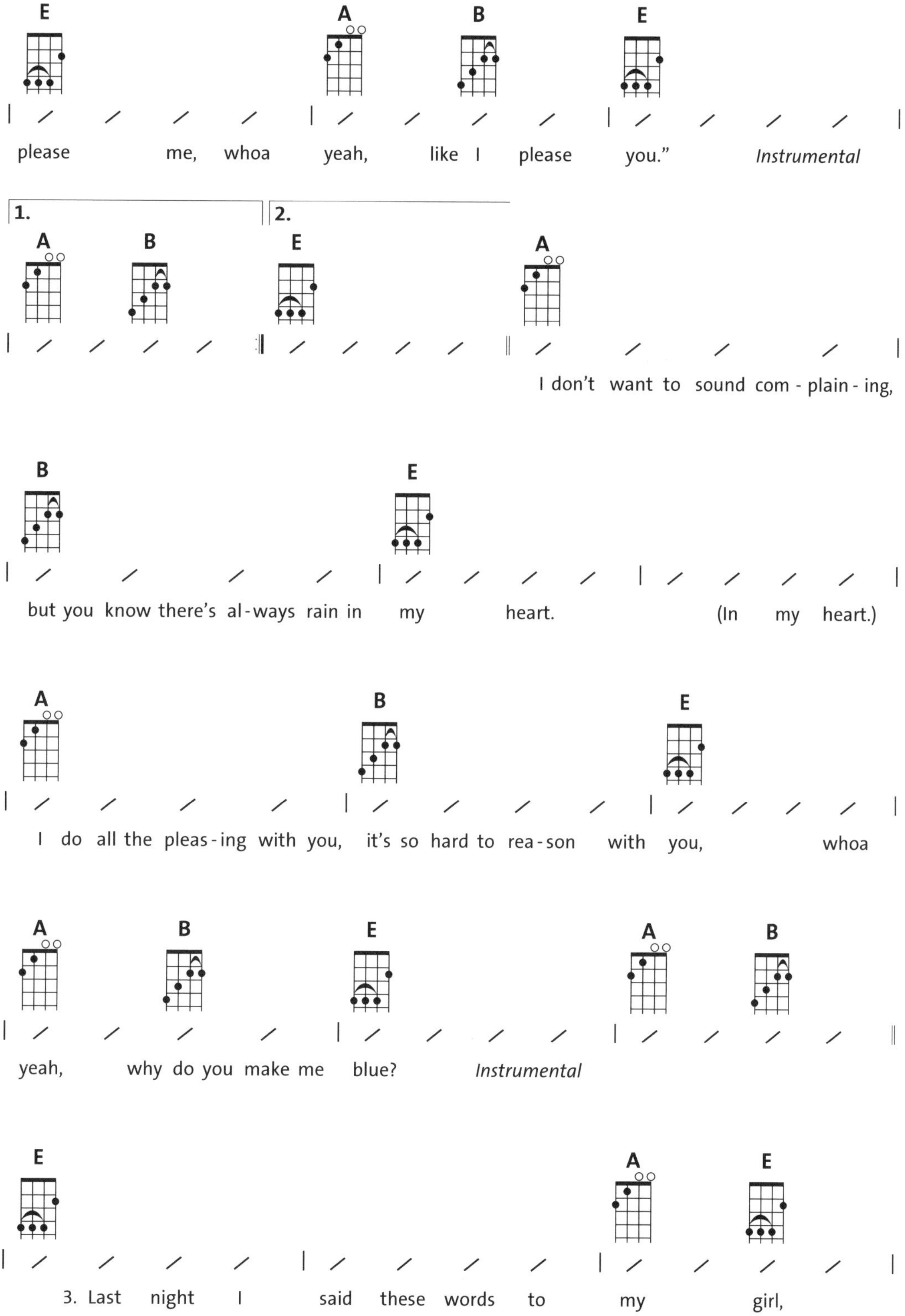
E A B E
please me, whoa yeah, like I please you." Instrumental
1. A B
2. E A
I don't want to sound com - plain - ing,
B E
but you know there's al - ways rain in my heart. (In my heart.)
A B E
I do all the pleas - ing with you, it's so hard to rea - son with you, whoa
A B E A B
yeah, why do you make me blue? Instrumental
E A E
3. Last night I said these words to my girl,

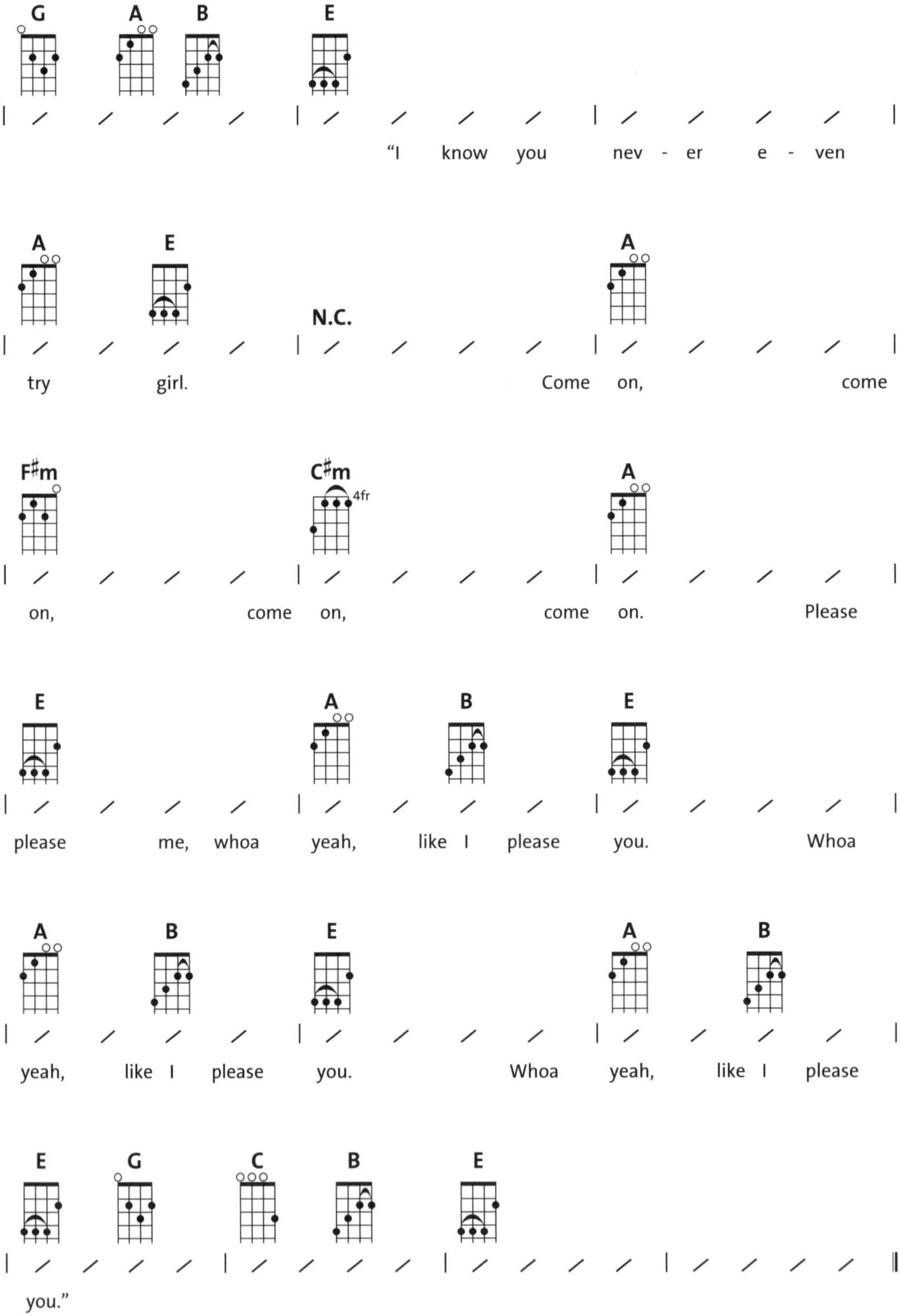
G A B E
"I know you nev - er e - ven
A E N.C. A
try girl. Come on, come
F♯m C♯m 4fr A
on, come on, come on. Please
E A B E
please me, whoa yeah, like I please you. Whoa
A B E A B
yeah, like I please you. Whoa yeah, like I please
E G C B E
you."

when i'm sixty four

Words & Music by John Lennon & Paul McCartney

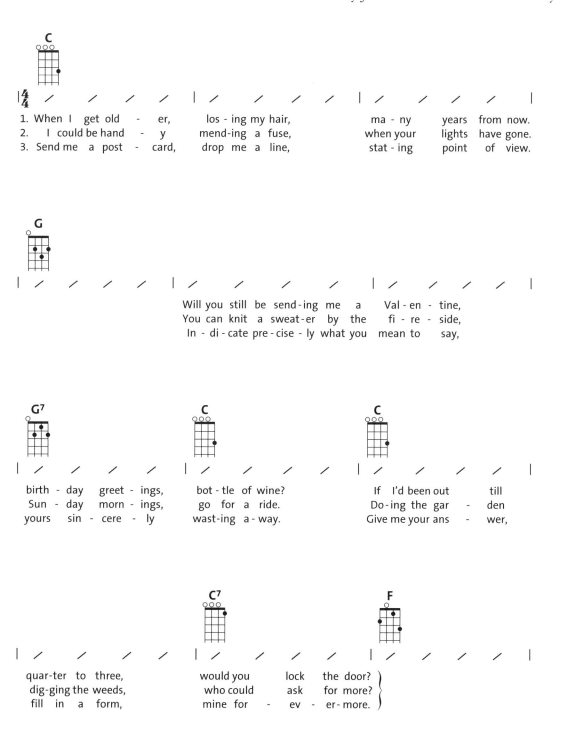

C

$\frac{4}{4}$

1. When I get old - er, los - ing my hair, ma - ny years from now.
2. I could be hand - y mend-ing a fuse, when your lights have gone.
3. Send me a post - card, drop me a line, stat - ing point of view.

G

Will you still be send-ing me a Val - en - tine,
You can knit a sweat-er by the fi - re - side,
In - di - cate pre-cise - ly what you mean to say,

G7 | **C** | **C**

birth - day greet - ings, bot - tle of wine? If I'd been out till
Sun - day morn - ings, go for a ride. Do-ing the gar - den
yours sin - cere - ly wast-ing a - way. Give me your ans - wer,

C7 | **F**

quar-ter to three, would you lock the door?
dig-ging the weeds, who could ask for more?
fill in a form, mine for - ev - er-more.

Fm C A7 D7 G7 *To Coda* ⊕

Will you still need me, will you still feed me, when I'm six - ty

C 1. Am

four? Oo,

G Am

you'll be

E7 Am

old - er too. Ah,
(Ah.)

Dm F

and if you say the word, I could

G C G7

stay with you.

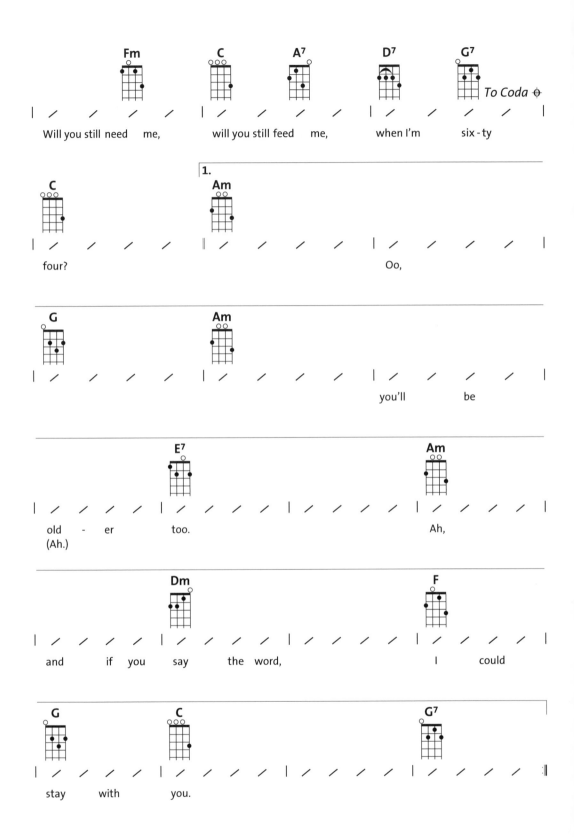

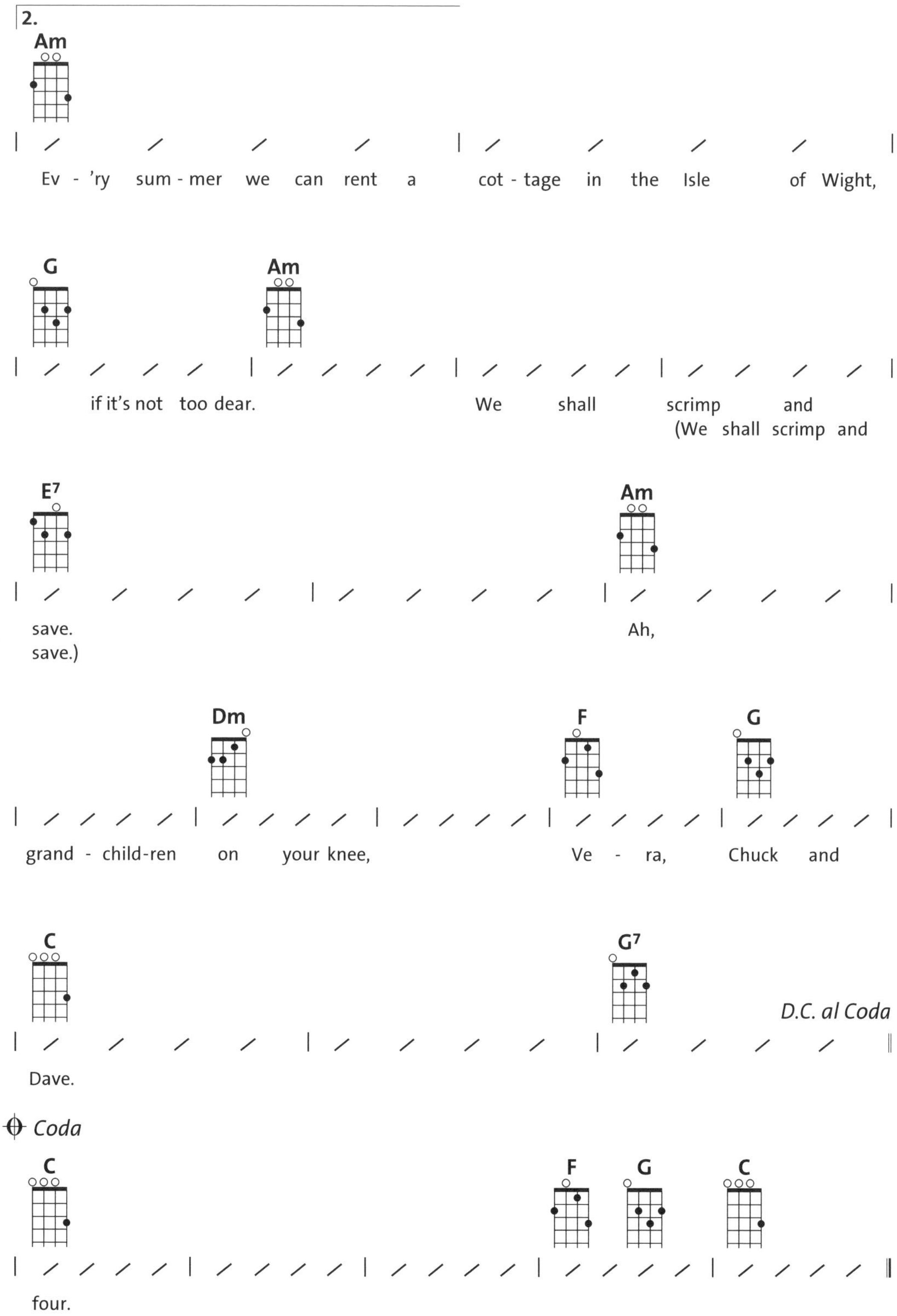
2.
Am
Ev - 'ry sum - mer we can rent a cot - tage in the Isle of Wight,
G Am
if it's not too dear. We shall scrimp and
(We shall scrimp and
E7 Am
save. Ah,
save.)
Dm F G
grand - child-ren on your knee, Ve - ra, Chuck and
C G7
D.C. al Coda
Dave.
Coda
C F G C
four.

yesterday

Words & Music by John Lennon & Paul McCartney

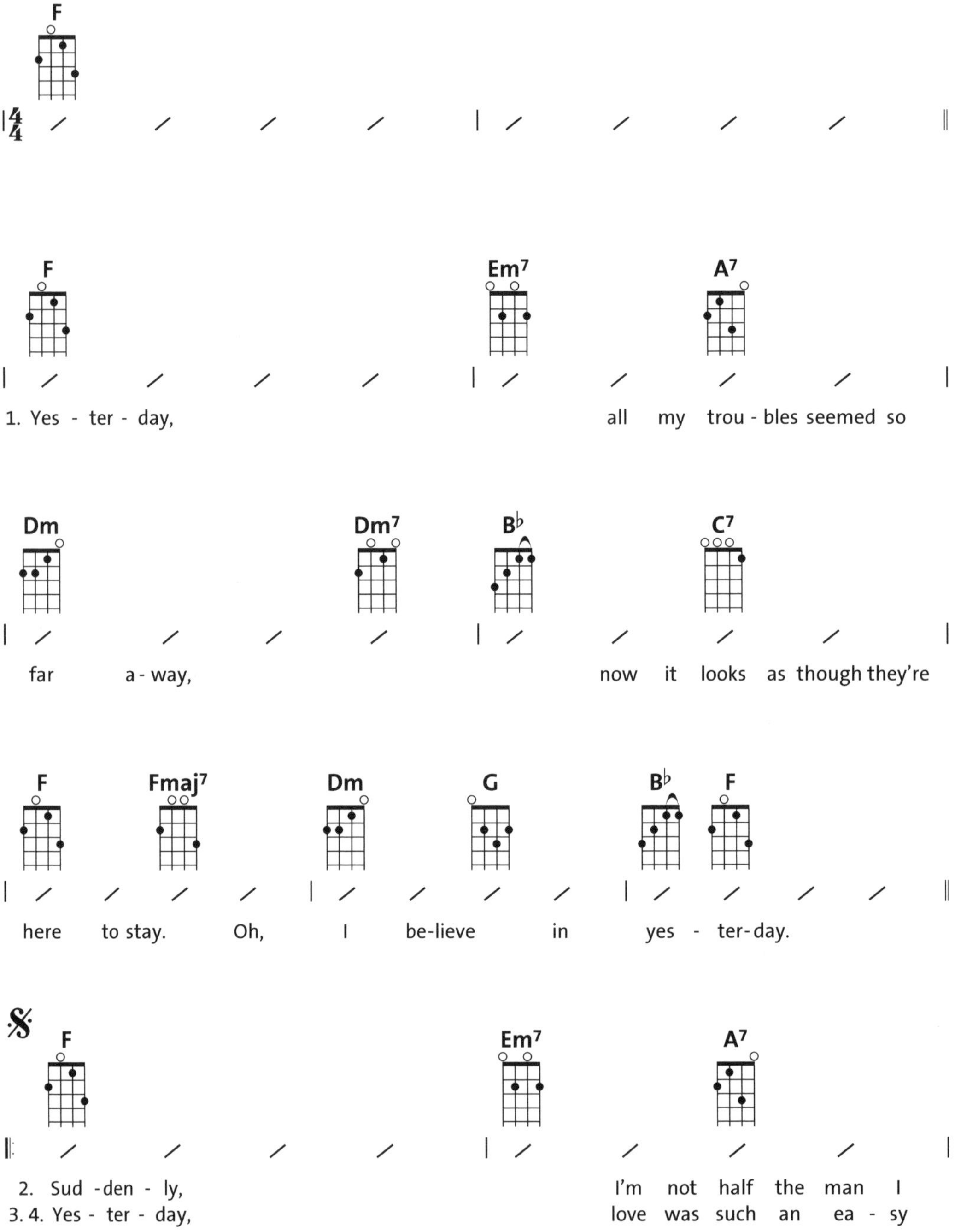
F
4/4
F
Em7
A7
1. Yes - ter - day,
all my trou - bles seemed so
Dm
Dm7
B♭
C7
far a - way,
now it looks as though they're
F
Fmaj7
Dm
G
B♭
F
here to stay. Oh, I be-lieve in yes - ter-day.
F
Em7
A7
2. Sud - den - ly,
3. 4. Yes - ter - day,
I'm not half the man I
love was such an ea - sy

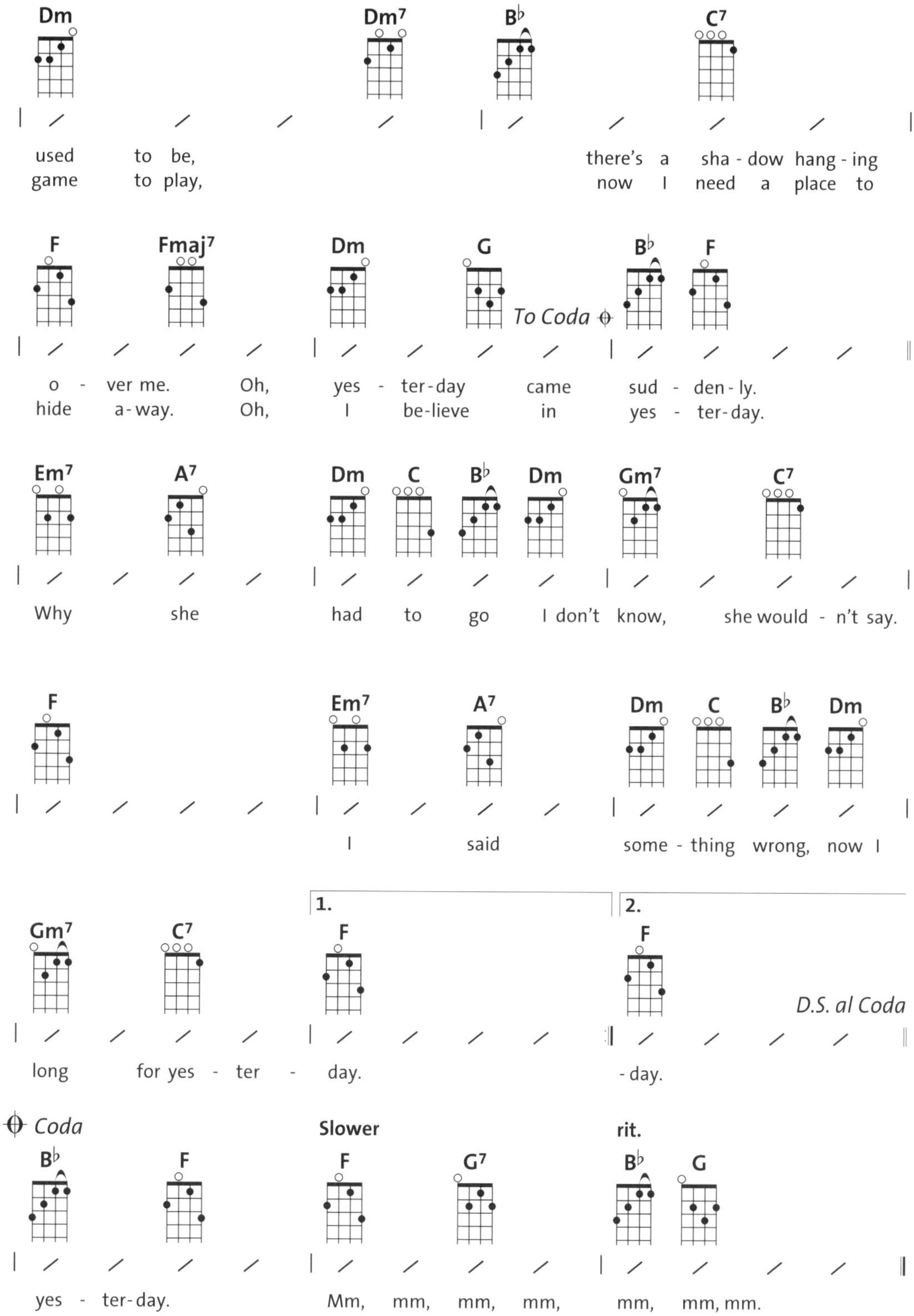
Dm Dm7 B♭ C7
used to be, there's a sha - dow hang - ing
game to play, now I need a place to
F Fmaj7 Dm G To Coda B♭ F
o - ver me. Oh, yes - ter-day came sud - den - ly.
hide a - way. Oh, I be-lieve in yes - ter-day.
Em7 A7 Dm C B♭ Dm Gm7 C7
Why she had to go I don't know, she would - n't say.
F Em7 A7 Dm C B♭ Dm
I said some - thing wrong, now I
Gm7 C7 1. F 2. F D.S. al Coda
long for yes - ter - day. - day.
Coda
Slower
rit.
B♭ F F G7 B♭ G
yes - ter-day. Mm, mm, mm, mm, mm, mm, mm.

your mother should know

Words & Music by John Lennon & Paul McCartney

Am / / / / | **F** / / / / |

1. 2. Let's all get up and dance to a song, that was a
3. Lift up your hearts and sing me a song, that was a
4. Da da da da da da da da da da da da

A7 / / / / | **Dm** / / / / |

hit be - fore your mo - ther was born.
hit be - fore your mo - ther was born.
da da da da da da da.

G7 / / / / | **C** / / / / | **A7** / / / / |

Though she was born a long, long time a - go, your mo-ther should know,

D7 / / / / | **G7** / / / / | **C** / / / / | *To Codas* ⊕

Your mo-ther should know.____
(Your mo - ther should Ah)

1. E7 / / / / :| **2. E** / / / / | $\frac{2}{4}$ / / | $\frac{4}{4}$ **Am** / / / / |

Sing it a - gain. *Instrumental*

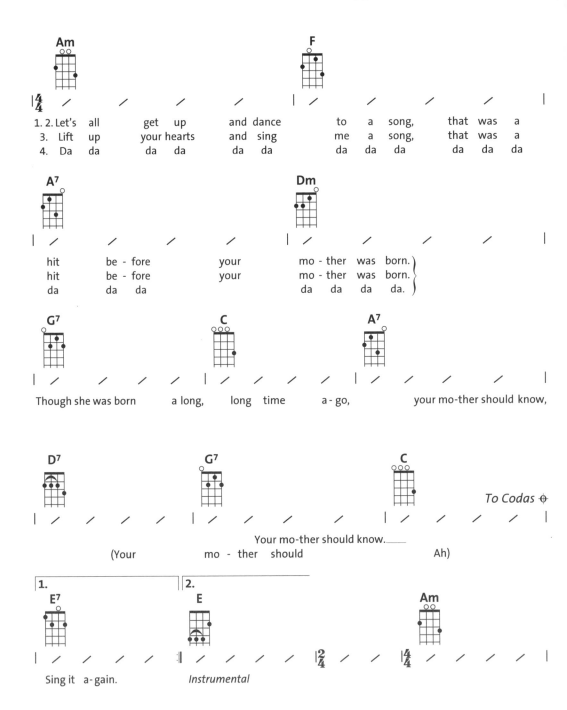

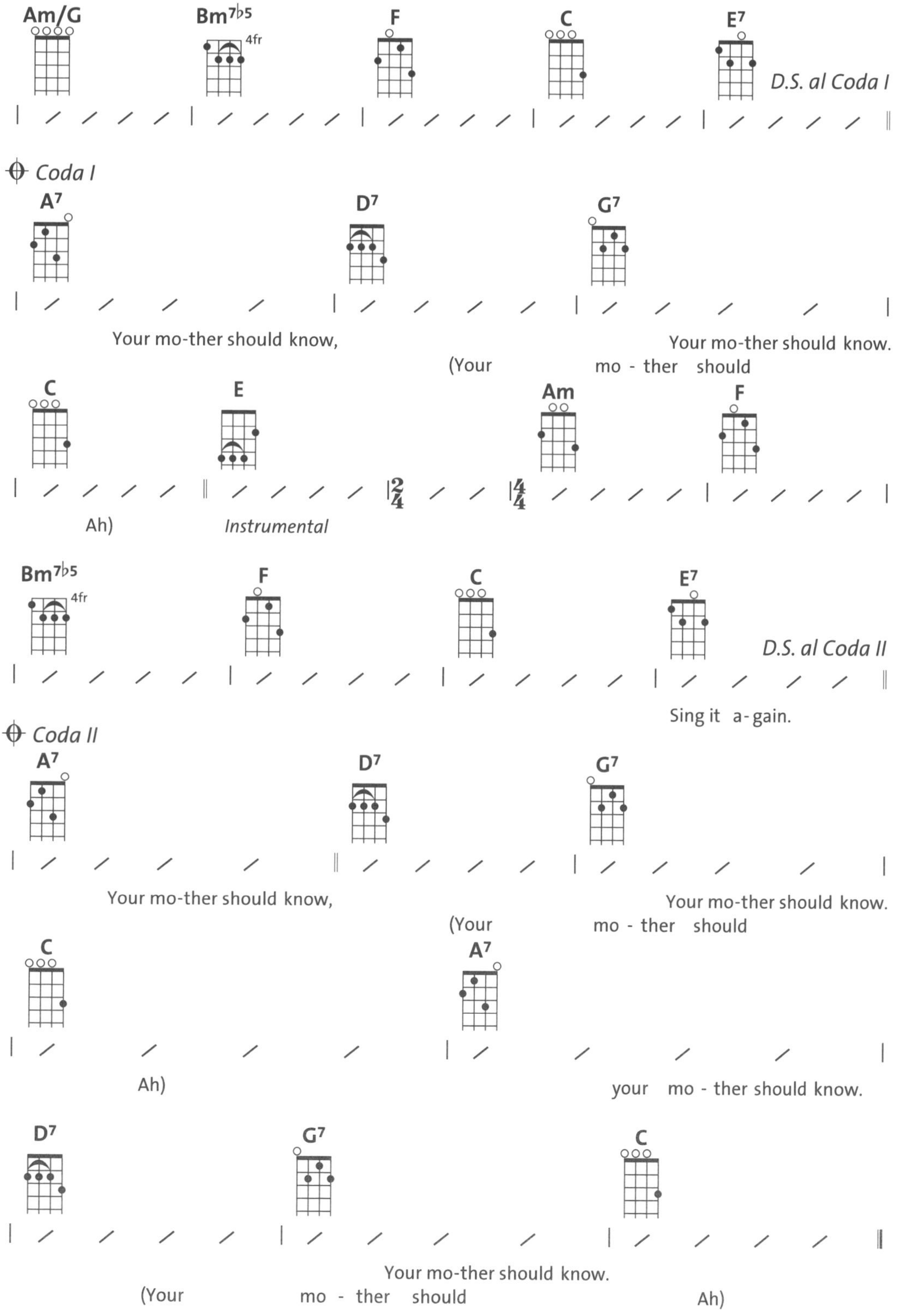
Am/G
Bm7♭5
4fr
F
C
E7
D.S. al Coda I
Coda I
A7
D7
G7
Your mo-ther should know,
Your mo-ther should know.
(Your mo - ther should
C
E
Am
F
2/4
4/4
Ah)
Instrumental
Bm7♭5
4fr
F
C
E7
D.S. al Coda II
Sing it a-gain.
Coda II
A7
D7
G7
Your mo-ther should know,
Your mo-ther should know.
(Your mo - ther should
C
A7
Ah)
your mo - ther should know.
D7
G7
C
Your mo-ther should know.
(Your mo - ther should
Ah)